W9-DBC-811

# TEACHER'S RESOURCE MANUAL
# CONCEPTS IN MODERN BIOLOGY

## DAVID KRAUS

**GLOBE FEARON EDUCATIONAL PUBLISHER**
Upper Saddle River, New Jersey
www.globefearon.com

## THE AUTHOR

DAVID KRAUS, B.S., MS. in Education; former Chairman of the Science Department, Far Rockaway High School, New York City. Member of the New York State Biology Syllabus Committee and President of the Biology Chairman's Association of New York City. Member of the Committee on Social Implications of Biology Teaching of the National Association of Biology Teachers. Winner of the NSTA STAR Teaching Award and designated as Teacher of the Year by the New York Biology Teachers Association. Served on curriculum project at Sloan-Kettering Institute and did research on Hydra at Adelphi University and at Boyce Thompson Institute. Founding member of New York Council for Evolution Education. Contributor to *The American Biology Teacher, The Science Teacher, Adaptation,* and *Creation/Evolution.*

**ISBN** 0-835-94840-4

Printed in the United States of America
1 2 3 4 5 6 7 8 9 10    02 01 00 99 98

**GLOBE FEARON EDUCATIONAL PUBLISHER**
Upper Saddle River, New Jersey
www.globefearon.com

# TABLE OF CONTENTS

**Correlation Between The Regents Biology
Syllabus And The Textbook** .......................................................... iv, v

**To The Teacher: How To Use Concepts in Modern Biology** ........................ vi

## Teacher's Guide to Chapters and Answers to Textbook Questions

**Unit One: Unity and Diversity Among Living Things** ............................... 1
    Chapter One ...................................................................... 1
    Chapter Two ...................................................................... 1
    Chapter Three .................................................................... 2
    Chapter Four ..................................................................... 3

**Unit Two: Maintenance in Living Things** 6
    Chapter Five ...................................................................... 6
    Chapter Six ....................................................................... 8
    Chapter Seven .................................................................... 10
    Chapter Eight .................................................................... 11
    Chapter Nine ..................................................................... 12
    Chapter Ten ...................................................................... 13

**Unit Three: Human Physiology** 15
    Chapter Eleven ................................................................... 15
    Chapter Twelve ................................................................... 16
    Chapter Thirteen ................................................................. 17
    Chapter Fourteen ................................................................ 18
    Chapter Fifteen .................................................................. 19
    Chapter Sixteen .................................................................. 20

**Unit Four: Reproduction and Development** 22
    Chapter Seventeen ............................................................... 22
    Chapter Eighteen ................................................................. 23
    Chapter Nineteen ................................................................ 24

**Unit Five: Genetics** 25
    Chapter Twenty ................................................................... 25
    Chapter Twenty-one .............................................................. 29
    Chapter Twenty-two .............................................................. 30

**Unit Six: Evolution** 32
    Chapter Twenty-three ............................................................ 32
    Chapter Twenty-four ............................................................. 33

**Unit Seven: Plants and Animals in Their Environment** 34
    Chapter Twenty-five .............................................................. 34
    Chapter Twenty-six ............................................................... 36

**Appendix: Answers to Laboratory Skills Review** ............................... 37

**Answers to Critical Thinking Questions** ...................................... 39

**Reproducible Masters: List of Illustrations** ................................. 47

**Critical Thinking Questions** ................................................. 71

# CORRELATION BETWEEN THE REGENTS BIOLOGY SYLLABUS AND THE TEXTBOOK

**NEW YORK STATE REGENTS BIOLOGY**                    **CONCEPTS IN MODERN BIOLOGY**

## UNIT I
### Core Topic: Unity and Diversity Among Living Things
Syllabus Objectives                                                    Textbook Chapters

The student should be able to:

| | |
|---|---|
| 1. Define life in terms of the functions performed by living organisms. | Chapter 1 |
| 2. Describe some of the schemes by which organisms are classified. | Chapter 2 |
| 3. Recognize the role of the cell as the basic unit of structure and function of most living things. | Chapter 3 |
| 4. Identify major biochemical compounds and some of the metabolic reactions in which these compounds are involved. | Chapter 4 |
| 5. Identify the appropriate tools and/or techniques used for cell study. | Chapter 3 |
| 6. Recognize that a unity of pattern underlies the diversity of living things. | Chapters 1 through 4 |

Unit I Extended Topics

| | |
|---|---|
| 1. Composition of Carbohydrates, Lipids, and Proteins | Chapter 4 |
| 2. Factors Influencing Enzyme Action | Chapter 4 |

## UNIT II
### Core Topic: Maintenance in Living Things
Syllabus Objectives:                                                   Textbook Chapters

The student should be able to:

| | |
|---|---|
| 1. Identify and describe the basic functions necessary to maintain homeostasis. | Chapters 5 through 10 |
| 2. Identify and compare the adaptations of selected organisms for carrying out these functions. | Chapters 5 through 10 |
| 3. Recognize that a unity of pattern underlies the diversity of living things. | Chapters 5 through 10 |
| 4. Correlate biochemical reactions with physiological functions. | Chapter 5, Chapters 7 through 9 |
| 5. Observe and recognize that structure and function complement each other and culminate in an organism's successful adaptation to its environment. | Chapters 5 through 10 |

Unit II Extended Topics

| | |
|---|---|
| Chemistry of light and dark reactions in photosynthesis | Chapter 5 |
| Chemistry of anaerobic and aerobic phases of respiration | Chapter 7 |

## UNIT III
### Core Topic: Human Physiology
Syllabus Objectives:                                                   Textbook Chapters

The student should be able to:

| | |
|---|---|
| 1. Recognize that humans are not unique in their performance of the functions necessary to maintain life. | Chapters 11 through 16 |
| 2. Apply scientific information to food choice decisions. | Chapter 11 |
| 3. Identify the major structures and functions of the human body and their role in the maintenance of homeostasis. | Chapters 11 through 16 |
| 4. Describe the interrelationships among the systems of the human body. | Chapters 11 through 16 |
| 5. Describe the structure and function of the major organs of the human body | Chapters 11 through 16 |

Unit III Extended Topics

| | |
|---|---|
| 1. Carbohydrates and protein in the diet | Chapter 11 |
| 2. Hydrolysis of carbohydrate, protein, and lipid molecules | Chapter 4 |
| 3. Digestive system malfunctions | Chapter 11 |
| 4. Blood clotting | Chapter 12 |
| 5. Immunity and Allergies | Chapter 12 |
| 6. Pulmonary and systemic circulation, coronary circulation, lymphatic circulation | Chapter 12 |
| 7. Cardiovascular disease | Chapter 12 |
| 8. Blood disease | Chapter 12 |
| 9. Respiratory system malfunctions | Chapter 13 |
| 10. Excretory system malfunctions | Chapter 14 |
| 11. Nervous system malfunctions | Chapter 15 |
| 12. Endocrine functional organization | Chapter 15 |
| 13. Malfunctions associated with locomotion | Chapter 16 |

## UNIT IV
### Core Topic: Reproduction and Development
Syllabus Objectives:                                       Textbook Chapters

| The student should be able to: | |
|---|---|
| 1. Describe the processes of mitosis, meiosis, and fertilization. | Chapters 17 through 19 |
| 2. Recognize the role of mitosis, meiosis, and fertilization in reproductive cycles. | Chapters 17 through 19 |
| 3. Compare the processes of asexual and sexual reproduction in terms of methods and results. | Chapters 17 through 19 |
| 4. Compare the adaptations for sexual reproduction and development in both plants and animals. | Chapters 17 through 19 |
| 5. Explain the relationships among numbers of eggs, methods of fertilization, and sites of embryonic development as they relate to species survival. | Chapter 18 |
| 6. Describe the development of plant and animal embryos. | Chapters 18 and 19 |
| 7. Describe hormonal interactions in the human male and female. | Chapter 18 |

Unit IV Extended Topics

| | |
|---|---|
| 1. External development of the vertebrate embryo | Chapter 18 |
| 2. Human reproduction and development | Chapter 18 |

## UNIT V
### Transmission of Traits from Generation to Generation
Syllabus Objectives:                                       Textbook Chapters

| The student should be able to: | |
|---|---|
| 1. Explain the transmission of genetic traits using the gene-chromosome theory. | Chapters 20 through 22 |
| 2. Predict the probable results of genetic crosses. | Chapters 20 and 22 |
| 3. Identify some patterns of inheritance by interpreting pedigree charts | Chapter 22 |
| 4. List various mutations and describe their consequences. | Chapters 20 and 22 |
| 5. List several practical applications of the principles of genetics. | Chapters 21 and 22 |
| 6. Recognize the role of heredity and environment in gene expression. | Chapters 20 through 22 |
| 7. Describe some techniques used in genetic research. | Chapters 20 through 22 |
| 8. Describe some genetically-related disorders in humans. | Chapters 20 and 22 |
| 9. Describe the basic structure of the DNA molecule and its role in heredity | Chapter 21 |
| 10. Explain changes in a population on the basis of the Hardy-Weinberg Principle. | Chapter 20 |

Unit V Extended Topics

| | |
|---|---|
| 1. Human genetic disorders | Chapter 22 |
| 2. Genetic control of cellular activities. | Chapter 21 |
| 3. Genetic research | Chapter 22 |
| 4. Population genetics | Chapter 20 |

## UNIT VI
### Core Topic: Evolution
Syllabus Objectives:                                       Textbook Chapters

| The student should be able to: | |
|---|---|
| 1. Understand that evolution is a process of change. | Chapters 23 and 24 |
| 2. Recognize that evolutionary theory is supported by observations and inferences from many branches of science. | Chapters 23 and 24 |
| 3. Describe some of the supporting data for evolutionary theory. | Chapter 23 |
| 4. Discuss the historical development of evolutionary theory. | Chapters 23 and 24 |
| 5. Describe a hypothesis which attempt to explain how primitive environmental conditions may have contributed to the formation of initial life forms. | Chapter 23 |

## UNIT VII
### Core Topic: Ecology
Syllabus Objectives                                       Textbook Chapters

| The student should be able to: | |
|---|---|
| 1. Describe the interdependency of organisms on each other and on their environment. | Chapter 25 |
| 2. Identify and define the ecological levels of organization of the living world. | Chapter 25 |
| 3. Identify and describe the components that form and maintain an ecosystem. | Chapter 25 |
| 4. Explain how interactions of living organisms with each other and their environment result in succession. | Chapter 25 |
| 5. Assess human influence on the balance of nature. | Chapter 26 |

Unit VII Extended Topics

| | |
|---|---|
| 1. Symbiotic relationships | Chapter25 |
| 2. Successional changes | Chapter 25 |
| 3. Biomes of the World | Chapter 25 |

# TO THE TEACHER

## How To Use The Concepts in Modern Biology Program

### How To Use The Student Textbook

*Concepts in Modern Biology* is organized into units and chapters that follow the organization of the Regents Biology Syllabus. Each chapter section begins with a letter, such as A, B, C, etc., and a title. Letters enclosed in a square, such as $\boxed{C}$, denote core material in the syllabus. Letters enclosed in a circle, such as $\text{Ⓒ}$, denote extended material in the syllabus.

The textbook also contains **laboratory skills** within some of the chapters. The lab skills are indicated by a color band on the margin of the page.

Some chapters contain extra material that is not referred to in the Regents Biology Syllabus. This material, which is indicated by a gray margin on the page, is included to challenge students who are ready to go beyond the syllabus. It will not detract from your use of the textbook if you choose to bypass this optional material.

### How To Use the Teacher's Resource Manual

This Teacher's Resource Manual contains a **guide** to using the 26 chapters in the textbook and **answers** to all chapter questions and reasoning exercises. This portion of the manual contains an **overview**, **motivation idea**, and **teaching suggestions** for each textbook chapter.

In addition, the manual contains:

- A set of **23 reproducible masters** with **illustrations** from the textbook. The illustrations on these masters do not have labels, and may be used for reinforcement, drill, or assessment. The illustration masters may be found on pp. 47–70.

- **Critical Thinking Questions** for each chapter are also provided as reproducible masters. Many of these questions relate directly to illustrations in the textbook, and will give your students experience in analyzing, and making inferences from, diagrams and pictures. The Critical Thinking Question reproducible masters begin on p. 71. Answers to the Critical Thinking Questions may be found on pp. 39–46 in this manual.

All of the masters are on perforated pages so that you may remove them from the manual.

- A chart that shows the correlation between the textbook chapters and the objectives of the Regents Biology Syllabus.

- Suggested laboratory exercises to develop the lab skills specified in the syllabus.

# TEACHER'S GUIDE TO CHAPTERS AND ANSWERS TO TEXTBOOK QUESTIONS

# UNIT ONE
# UNITY AND DIVERSITY AMONG LIVING THINGS

Unit One provides an overview of the life functions that unite all living things and an examination of cell structure and chemical performance as the basis of these functions. Classification schemes are introduced and explained to demonstrate the diversity of life.

# CHAPTER 1
# THE CONCEPT OF LIFE

## Overview
The core material in Chapter 1 presents an explanation of basic life processes and homeostasis.

## Motivation
Display a variety of living and nonliving things, such as a goldfish in a bowl, a green plant, a lichen, a bacterial culture, moldy bread, a rock, a fossil, a nail, and a glass of water. Ask students which items are alive.

## Teaching Suggestions
1. Discuss why certain of the items displayed for the Motivation are living and others are nonliving. As students mention food-getting, respiration, and movement as functions of living things, lead them to understand that life can be defined in terms of these life processes. Point out that biology is the study of life.

2. Ask students to suggest ways in which different life processes may be coordinated to maintain homeostasis. As an example, students may mention sweating or shivering to maintain body temperature.

3. As students read the chapter, you may wish to have them complete the Chapter 1 Critical Thinking Questions on p. 71. Discuss answers after students have finished.

## ANSWERS TO CHAPTER 1 QUESTIONS

### Reasoning Exercises (Page 3)
1. Biology is the study of living things.

2. Breathing is not the same as respiration. Respiration is the process of releasing energy from food by oxidation. Breathing is merely one step in respiration, as carried on by some animals, and consists of moving air in and out of the body.

3. Homeostasis is the maintenance of a stable internal environment by organisms.

4. Eight life functions are: nutrition, transport, respiration, excretion, synthesis, regulation, growth, and reproduction.

### Completion Questions (Page 4)
A 1. biology 2. life functions 3. all B 4. nutrition
5. photosynthesis 6. transport 7. circulatory system
8. respiration 9. excretion 10. regulation
11. metabolism 12. homeostasis 13. scientific method
14. data 15. scientific processes

### Multiple-Choice Questions (Page 5)
A-B 1. (2) 2. (1) 3. (3) 4. (2) 5. (3) 6. (2)
7. (1) 8. (3) 9. (3) 10. (1) 11. (4) 12. (2) 13. (2)
14. (3) 15. (3) 16. (4) 17. (3)

### Chapter Test (Page 6)
1. (4) 2. (3) 3. (1) 4. (2) 5. (2) 6. (b) 7. (a) 8. (c)
9. (a) 10. (d)

# CHAPTER 2
# THE DIVERSITY OF LIFE

## Overview
The core material in Chapter 2 introduces the five-kingdom classification scheme and the binomial system of nomenclature. The extended material provides a detailed examination of the major phyla.

## Motivation
Invite students to name a variety of living things. List several examples on the chalkboard. Then ask students to suggest how they might classify these examples. Encourage students to use what they know about the examples listed to discuss briefly what any of them might have in common,

## Teaching Suggestions
1. Introduce the five-kingdom classification system

to demonstrate evolutionary developments without having students memorize a detailed taxonomic scheme. Present as many living specimens as possible. For example, use a microprojector to show living protozoa, algae, nematodes, brine shrimp, *Hydra*, *Daphnia*, and *Planaria*. If possible, organize a field trip to a vacant lot or the school grounds to point out living specimens.

2. You may also want to investigate the resources of local museums, zoological and botanical gardens, and nature centers. Organize a field trip to one of these places and prepare a "trail guide" to highlight pertinent exhibits. Find out in advance if the place you plan to visit has printed materials or other resources about the diversity of organisms that can be observed.

3. To illustrate the subdivision of genera into species, display leaves from various species of trees in your area. For example, you might use silver maple, red maple, sugar maple, Norway maple, and box elder.

4. If you go into some depth on "The Roll Call of Living Things," conduct a lab practicum. Set out specimens of living things on numbered lab tables, with questions alongside each specimen for students to answer. Start a group at each table. Use a buzzer or an oral signal for groups to proceed to the next table. One exhibit could consist of a mirror concealed by a piece of cardboard marked "Raise to see specimen."

5. Have students complete Chapter 2 Critical Thinking Questions on p.71 while they read the chapter. As an example of how taxonomy is an ongoing science, you may wish to point out that in 1985 chemical research on DNA and protein structures determined that the giant panda is a bear while the red panda is a raccoon.

## ANSWERS TO CHAPTER 2 QUESTIONS

### Reasoning Exercises (Page 11)
1. A worldwide name for each organism permits scientists from various countries to understand each other when referring to living things.
2. Taxonomy is the science of classification. Modern taxonomy is the attempt to classify organisms on the basis of their evolutionary relationships.
3. The three-kingdom classification sets apart, as a

separate kingdom, the protists which have cellular characteristics of both plants and animals. The four-kingdom classification sets apart the monerans whose cells lack a distinct nucleus. The two-kingdom system is rarely used for scientific purposes today because microscopic and biochemical techniques have identified new, fundamental differences among living things.
4. Mules are not considered to be a species because they cannot mate to produce fertile offspring.
5. From an organism's complete scientific name you can learn its genus and species and the name of its discoverer.

### Reasoning Exercises (Page 38)
1. Cells of the prokaryotes lack a well-defined nucleus and nuclear membrane. Cells of the eukaryotes have a distinct nucleus.
2. The tracheophytes have vascular tubes to carry water upward.
3. Porifera—bath sponge; Coelenterata—*Hydra*; Platyhelminthes—*Planaria*; Nematoda—*Trichinella*; Annelida—earthworm; Mollusca—snail; Arthropoda—crab; Echinodermata—starfish.
4. Chordates have a dorsal notochord, paired-gill slits, a dorsal tubular nerve cord, and a post-anal tail.
5. Mammals have mammary glands and hair, and give birth to living young.

### Completion Questions (Page 38)
A-B  1. taxonomy  2. extinct  3. evolution
C  4. Monera  5. blue-green algae  6. Protista
7. Chordata  8. plant  9. fungi  10. species
D  11. classes  12. scientific  13. binomial
E  14. monerans  15. staphyloccocus  16. alga
17. tracheophytes  18. monocots  19. bilateral
20. segment (proglottid)  21. regeneration  22. notochord

### Multiple-Choice Questions (Page 39)
A-B  1. (3)  2. (4)    C  3. (1)  4. (3)  5. (3)  6. (4)  7. (1)
D  8. (1)  9. (2)  10. (3)  11. (3)  12. (4)    E  13. (1)
14. (3)

### Chapter Test (Page 40)
1. (2)  2. (1)  3. (4)  4. (4)  5. (4)  6. (2)  7. (3)  8. (1)
9. (1)  10. (1)

## ◼ CHAPTER 3
## THE UNITY OF LIFE

### Overview
The core material in Chapter 3 presents the cell theory and a description of cell structure.

### Motivation
Ask students what they think is the basic unit of life that all living things share. Provide the answer if students do not mention the cell. Then ask students how

scientists are able to study cells, which are too small to see with the eye alone.

### Teaching Suggestions
1. Distribute the reproducible masters *An Animal Cell* and *A Plant Cell* for students to compare. If available, display scanning electron microscope photographs of the detailed structure of cells. Possible resources are *Scanning*

*Electron Microscopy in Biology: A Student's Atlas of Biological Organization,* by R. Kessel and G. Shih, Springer-Verlag Inc., 1974, and *Scanning Electron Microscopy of Cells in Culture,* edited by Paul B. Bell, Jr., Springer-Verlag, Inc., 1984.

**2.** Before students study cells in a lab exercise, show them a film or videotape of live cells to demonstrate cell movement.

**3.** To show the action of one-celled organisms, demonstrate the "mercury pseudopod." On an overhead projector, place some dilute nitric acid in a petri dish and add a drop of mercury. *(Caution: Use appropriate safety measures in handling mercury and dilute nitric acid.)* Place a crystal of potassium dichromate near the drop of mercury. "Pseudopods" will form. If you gently stir the nitric acid with an iron nail, "fission" will occur. (Adapted from a suggestion by Laura Martland and Joel Seller published in the *Journal of New York Biology Teachers Association,* Winter 1982, page 15.)

**4.** To illustrate exceptions to the cell theory, use charts, overhead transparencies, or microprojections of muscle cells, slime mold, and bread mold. Find pictures of viruses in *Scientific American, Discover,* or *Science News.*

**5.** You may wish to have students study reproducible master *The Compound Microscope* when you discuss the use of the microscope. Invite students to refer to their diagram as they point to and identify the parts of a compound microscope.

**6.** To illustrate the importance of staining to distinguish cell structures through a microscope, dip a clear plastic rod into glycerin or immersion oil. Have students note that the immersed portion seems to disappear. Explain that light is affected by the rod and the oil in the same way because they have the same refractive index. Then show that a colored rod can be seen in the oil.

**7.** As students read the chapter, you may wish to have them complete Chapter 3 Critical Thinking Questions on p. 72.

## ANSWERS TO CHAPTER 3 QUESTIONS

### Reasoning Exercises (Page 47)
**1.** A simple microscope has one set of lenses and a compound microscope has two sets of lenses.
**2.** The cell theory states: (1) The cell is the unit of structure of plants and animals. (2) The cell is the unit of function of plants and animals. (3) All cells arise from preexisting living cells.

**3.** By focusing downward you may push the objective into the slide and damage the slide and/or the objective. Prevent this outcome by lowering the objective while looking at it from the side and then focusing upward while looking through the eyepiece.
**4.** The resolving power is the ability to distinguish between two points that are very close together.
**5.** The length of the cell is 1/4 of 1,400 $\mu$m, or 350 $\mu$m.

### Reasoning Exercises (Page 56)
**1.** When a cell dies, the lysosomes digest the cell contents.
**2.** A cell cannot live long without a nucleus because the nucleus is responsible for regulating the life activities of the cell.
**3.** Chromosomes are composed of protein and DNA. They control the activity of the cell and pass on the cell's heredity to succeeding generations of cells.
**4.** A typical plant cell has a cell wall, large vacuoles, and chloroplasts (if it is a green plant cell) but it has no centrosome. A typical animal cell does not have cell walls or chloroplasts but does have a centrosome; its vacuoles are generally small.
**5.** The cell membrane consists of a lipid bilayer in which large protein molecules float. It encloses the contents of plant and animal cells and controls the passage of materials into and out of the cells. The cell wall is an additional layer, composed mainly of cellulose, that surrounds the cell membrane of plant cells and of some protists. The cell wall permits most molecules to enter the cell.

### Completion Questions (page 56)
[A] **1.** Janssen **2.** Leeuwenhoek **3.** Virchow **4.** Schleiden and Schwann [B] **5.** 43X **6.** diaphragm **7.** light **8.** closer to **9.** phase-contrast microscope **10.** resolution **11.** centrifuge **12.** magnets **3.** 0.34 [C] **14.** endoplasmic reticulum **15.** selectively permeable **16.** ribosomes **17.** mitochondria **18.** secretion **19.** lysosomes **20.** chloroplasts **21.** centrosome **22.** cellulose **23.** cyclosis [D] **24.** virus **25.** slime mold

### Multiple-Choice Questions (Page 57)
[A] **1.** (2) **2.** (1) **3.** (1) **4.** (3) **5.** (1) [B] **6.** (2) **7.** (4) **8.** (4) **9.** (1) **10.** (3) [C] **11.** (2) **12.** (3) **13.** (2) **14.** (3) **15.** (4) **16.** (2) **17.** (4) **18.** (3) [D] **19.** (3) **20.** (2)

### Chapter Test (Page 58)
**1.** (1) **2.** (2) **3.** (1) **4.** (3) **5.** (3) **6.** (4) **7.** (4) **8.** (3) **9.** (4) **10.** (2) **11.** (1) **12.** (1)

# CHAPTER 4
# THE CHEMISTRY OF LIVING THINGS

## Overview
The core material in Chapter 4 discusses atoms, molecules, and chemical bonds, and presents the characteristics of proteins, carbohydrates, fats, nucleic acids, and enzymes.

## Motivation
Invite students to picture thousands of people running together at the beginning of the New York Marathon. Ask them what is being expended to create this

movement. Point out that the basis of this great amount of energy lies in chemical and metabolic reactions.

## Teaching Suggestions

**1.** Before students begin Chapter 4, expose them to the use and interpretation of indicators, such as pH paper. See Lab Skill 8 in the Appendix. For handling bases and acids, have students read "Safety in the use of chemicals" in Lab Skill 11.

**2.** Use atomic and molecular models to demonstrate chemical action. For example, dehydration synthesis of a dipeptide can be shown with a ball-and-stick model. If commercial models are available, have students construct models of methane, ethane, ethanol, propane, propanol, isopropanol, glycine, glycylglycine, glucose, and maltose.

**3.** To demonstrate neutralization, change water into "wine" by pouring a flask of water containing phenolphthalein into a flask containing a few drops of dilute sodium hydroxide. Change the "wine" back into water by pouring it into another flask containing a few drops of dilute hydrochloric acid. Students will be able to explain how this is done later in the lesson. (*Caution: Use appropriate care in handling acids and bases.*)

**4.** To help students relate organic chemistry to more concrete examples, display samples of common materials when discussing carbohydrates, fats, and proteins. Suggested samples are molasses, sucrose, flour, wood, olive oil, chicken fat, muscle from meat, and human hair.

**5.** Demonstrate the concept of complex sugars or nucleic acids as long-chain polymers by stringing beads. Point out that the string of beads represents the polymer. Then have a student cut the string. Point out that this action shows an enzyme breaking up the polymer. Indicate that the loose beads represent the individual building blocks of the polymer.

**6.** To demonstrate hydrolysis, add Benedict's solution to a solution of sucrose. Point out that the solution remains clear because sucrose is a disaccharide. Then boil a sucrose solution with a drop of dilute HCl. The sucrose will hydrolyze to simple sugars (glucose and fructose) and will then yield a positive result with Benedict's solution. (*Caution: Making the solution too acidic interferes with the action of Benedict's solution, which contains sodium carbonate.*)

**7.** For another hydrolysis demostration, prepare starch-agar plates by boiling 15 grams of agar and 10 grams of starch in a liter of water. Pour into petri dishes and allow to harden. (*Note: Sterilization is not necessary if the prepared plates are stored in a refrigerator.*) Streak saliva across part of the starch-agar preparations. After a minute, flood the dishes with dilute Lugol's solution. Display the dishes against the light from a window. Point out that the colorless part is where the saliva acted on the starch.

**8.** Use overhead transparencies to show the arrangement of amino acids in a protein, such as the human growth hormone. To show students an example of protein, extract casein from milk. Boil a cup of whole milk in a pan and add a tablespoon of vinegar or lemon juice to coagulate. Lift the casein from the pan with a strainer. To indicate the size of a protein molecule, write the empirical formula for casein on the chalkboard: $C_{708}H_{1130}O_{224}N_{180}S_4P_4$.

**9.** To illustrate that enzymes vary in their optimum pH, point out that digestion in the stomach takes place in an acid medium, whereas digestion in the small intestine takes place in a basic (alkaline) medium. Explain that the pH of stomach acid is 1, which is about the same as lime juice, and is more acidic than "acid rain," vinegar, cola, and tomatoes.

**10.** Demonstrate the action of catalysts and enzymes by these reactions:

- Hydrogen peroxide and iron filings. Note the bubbles of gas produced. (Use 20% $H_2O_2$, which can be purchased in the hair bleach section of a pharmacy, if not otherwise available.)
- Hydrogen peroxide and yeast cells. Test for oxygen with a glowing splint.
- Hydrogen peroxide and raw liver.
- Hydrogen peroxide and boiled liver (will not release oxygen).
- Hydrogen peroxide and liver that has been immersed in concentrated HCl (will not release oxygen). (*Caution: Use appropriate safety measures in handling acids.*)

Explain that yeast cells and raw liver contain the enzyme *catalase*, which breaks down harmful concentrations of peroxide in cells as it is formed. Hydrogen peroxide poured on a cut is broken down by the catalase present in the tissues to release oxygen, which kills bacteria. The bubbling action is also presumably helpful in removing bacteria. On intact skin, hydrogen peroxide does not make contact with catalase and does not form bubbles.

## ANSWERS TO CHAPTER 4 QUESTIONS

### Reasoning Exercises (Page 67)

**1.** (*a*) proton, neutron, (*b*) electron, (*c*) proton

**2.**

$_2$He$^4$ (helium)     $_3$Li$^7$ (lithium)     $_4$Be$^{10}$ (beryllium)

$_5$B$^{11}$ (boron)     $_7$N$^{14}$ (nitrogen)     $_{12}$Mg$^{24}$ (magnesium)

**3.** Three isotopes of hydrogen are protium, deuterium, and tritium. Isotopes are atoms that have the same atomic number but different atomic weights. Stable isotopes are identified by use of the mass spectrometer.
**4.** Soup—mixture; salt—compound; air—mixture; uranium—element; hydrogen—element; sodium chloride—compound.
**5.** Ionic bonds result from the transfer of electrons. Covalent bonds result from the sharing of electrons.

## Reasoning Exercises (Page 83)

**1.** Water is essential to life because chemical reactions within living things depend upon the presence of water.
**2.** See Fig. 4-14 in the textbook. "R" represents any of a number of groups of atoms that may fit into the general formula and substitute for a hydrogen atom.
**3.** Glycine + alanine $\rightarrow$ glycylalanine + water.
**4.** See Fig. 4-17 and Fig. 4-20 in the textbook.
**5.** In dehydration synthesis between two molecules of $C_6H_{12}O_6$, one molecule of $H_2O$ is removed.
**6.** Three fatty acids + glycerol $\rightarrow$ fat + $3H_2O$. The carbon atoms in the R group of a saturated fat have taken up all the hydrogen atoms that they can and there are no double bonds between these carbon atoms. In an unsaturated fat, the carbon atoms of the R group can

still take on more hydrogen atoms; the bonds that would have been used to attach hydrogen atoms are instead used to bond to other carbon atoms, resulting in double bonds between some carbon atoms.

## Completion Questions (Page 83)

$\boxed{\text{A}}$ **1.** isotopes **2.** neutron **3.** tracer, or tagged atom
**4.** compounds $\boxed{\text{B}}$ **5.** covalent **6.** ion **7.** structural
$\boxed{\text{C}}$ **8.** carbon **9.** amino acids **10.** dipeptide **11.** dehydration synthesis **12.** maltose **13.** glycerol **14.** nucleotide
**15.** nucleic acids **16.** deoxyribose **17.** phosphate or phosphoric acid **18.** complementary $\boxed{\text{D}}$ **19.** substrate
**20.** specific **21.** lock and key **22.** induced fit
**23.** inhibitors

## Multiple-Choice Questions (Page 84)

$\boxed{\text{A}}$ **1.** (3) **2.** (2) $\boxed{\text{B}}$ **3.** (4) **4.** (2) $\boxed{\text{C}}$ **5.** (4) **6.** (3)
**7.** (4) **8.** (2) **9.** (4) $\boxed{\text{D}}$ **10.** (2) **11.** (2) **12.** (3) **13.** (2)
**14.** (4) **15.** (3) **16.** (2) **17.** (3)

## Chapter Test (Page 85)

**1.** (2) **2.** (1) **3.** (1) **4.** (1) **5.** (3) **6.** (3) **7.** (3) **8.** (1)
**9.** (C) **10.** (E) **11.** (A) **12.** (B) **13.** (A) **14.** (4) **15.** (3)
**16.** (3) **17.** (2)

## Unit 1 Portfolio Project

Students may use a variety of methods, such as a Venn diagram, a checklist, or a three-column table labeled "Animal, Both, Plant." Diagrams should show:

■ Both have: cytoplasm, vacuole, golgi apparatus, endoplasmic reticulum, nucleus, nuclear membrane, ribosomes, nucleolus, mitochondria, lysosome, cell membrane
■ Plant cell has: cell wall, chloroplast, plastids, large vacuoles
■ Animal cell has: centrosome, centrioles, small vacuoles, microtubules, microfilaments

# UNIT TWO
# MAINTENANCE IN LIVING THINGS

Unit Two examines the basic maintenance functions living organisms perform: nutrition, transport, respiration, excretion, regulation, and locomotion.

Adaptations for carrying out these functions are illustrated by studying five representative organisms.

# CHAPTER 5
# NUTRITION

## Overview

The core material in Chapter 5 describes nutrition in plants and animals in two parts: *autotrophic nutrition* and *heterotrophic nutrition*. The extended material presents the biochemistry of light and dark reactions in photosynthesis.

## Motivation

Invite students to imagine a restaurant in which all living organisms could order a meal. Ask students to suggest what might be on the menu for a plant, an insect, a frog, a fish, a moose, a wolf, and a human. Discuss how these meals might be eaten. Point out that all organisms must get food to stay alive, but that the types of food and methods of obtaining it vary greatly.

## Teaching Suggestions

**1.** Because students may already be familiar with classical demonstrations of photosynthesis, select from the four experiments on textbook pages 90–91 to meet your class needs. These demonstrations provide an opportunity for valuable practice in the scientific method if the controls are emphasized. Encourage students to suggest controls and to criticize those that are used.

**2.** If your school has a spectrophotometer, demonstrate the preparation of an absorption spectrum of chlorophyll. Guide individual students in making readings at different wavelengths. Record student observations on the chalkboard and discuss.

**3.** To show that light can cause a chemical reaction, expose negative film, photographic paper and developer, or blueprint paper. Also display fabrics that have been faded by light.

**4.** When teaching photolysis, use the Hoffman electrolysis apparatus to show that water can be broken down by electrical energy.

**5.** To compare the effectiveness of different colors of light in promoting plant growth, have students grow young bean plants in milk cartons. Remove the carton tops and place a different colored cellophane sheet over each carton.

**6.** To demonstrate that white light is a mixture of various colors, use a color mixer from your Physics Department. You can also show the dispersion of light by beaming light through a prism after students have completed Critical Thinking Question 1 on p. 73. Point out that plants absorb blue and red wavelengths and reflect green, which makes plants appear green.

**7.** You can show that *Elodea* releases oxygen during photosynthesis by introducing white phosphorus to *Elodea* in a glass tube to produce clouds of white phosphorus pentoxide ($P_2O_5$) inside the tube. Be sure to set up this demonstration before class begins. Use a piece of glass tubing about 1 inch wide and 6 inches long, fitted with cork stoppers. (*Caution: This is a teacher demonstration. Do not touch white phosphorus nor allow students to have access to it.*)

Insert the bottom cork, place a sprig or two of *Elodea* inside the tube, and add sufficient water to leave a 3/4-inch air space at the top (see illustration). Pin a tiny cube of white phosphorus (about 3 ml on a side) to the top cork. Stopper the tube so that the phosphorus is inside the air space. The phosphorus will combine with the available oxygen and produce clouds of $P_2O_5$. When the oxygen is used up, the $P_2O_5$ will dissolve in the water and disappear. Invert the tube so that the phosphorus is submerged. Place the tube in light for about an hour. Then turn the tube upright so that the phosphorus is again in the air space. Clouds of phosphorus pentoxide will again appear in reaction to the additional oxygen produced by photosynthesis. Ask the class to suggest appropriate controls.

**8.** Demonstrate transpiration by placing a potted geranium plant under a bell jar or a under clear plastic bag tied around the plant stem. Seal the flowerpot and the soil by wrapping them with aluminum foil. Droplets of water will condense on the inner wall of the jar or bag. As a control, use a pot with soil but no plant. You may also introduce a cobalt chloride test paper strip, which turns from blue to pink in the presence of moisture. You can make your own test strips by soaking filter paper in a solution of cobalt chloride. Dry the paper and cut into strips.

**9.** Display a starch-agar petri dish inoculated with bread mold. Flood the plate with iodine solution to show that starch near the mold has been digested. You may also wish to use starch-digesting bacteria, such as *Pseudomonas saccharophila*.

**10.** Show the need for digestion by demonstrating how glucose can pass through a membrane but starch cannot. Place a concentrated glucose solution in one test tube

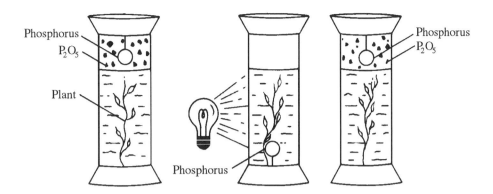

Does a green plant in the light produce oxygen? Use white phosphorus to detect the formation of oxygen.

and a starch suspension in another. Cover each tube with a cellophane membrane secured with a rubber band. Using a ring stand and clamps, invert each tube into a separate beaker containing a small volume of warm water. After several minutes, test the water for sugar or starch. See Lab Skill 8 in the textbook Appendix for tests on sugar and starch.

**11.** With the class, design a controlled experiment to determine whether saliva can change starch into sugar. Invite student volunteers to demonstrate the procedure. Outline the proposed steps on the chalkboard, including the following:

■ Test the supposed starch suspension for starch.
■ Test the supposed starch suspension for sugar.
■ Test the saliva for sugar.
■ Mix the starch suspension and saliva.
■ Test the mixture for sugar.

As an alternative, you may wish to use a soda cracker instead of the starch suspension. The importance of controls is highlighted if the cracker actually contains some sugar. The results are more dramatic if all the sugar tests are performed at one time using a hot water bath.

**12.** When discussing the concept of the digestive system as a "tube-within-a-tube," have students use the reproducible master of Figures 5-17 and 10-8 on p.51. This master illustrates the alimentary canal of the earthworm.

## ANSWERS TO CHAPTER 5 QUESTIONS

### Reasoning Exercises (Page 95)

**1.** Autotrophic nutrition is the process of getting food by synthesizing low-energy molecules into high-energy molecules. Heterotrophic nutrition requires other organisms as a source of high-energy food molecules.

**2.** In photosynthesis, energy is supplied by light. In chemosynthesis, energy is supplied by chemical reactions.

**3.** Photosynthesis supplies the food that most living things use for energy. At the same time, photosynthesis releases oxygen so that other organisms may carry on aerobic respiration.

**4.** The presence or absence of chlorophyll serves as a single variable while all other parts of the setup are the same. The experiment thus has a good control.

**5.** An object is blue because it absorbs all wavelengths except blue, which it reflects. Since a blue object absorbs the wavelengths for red, it does not reflect any wavelengths when placed in a red light—and thus it appears black.

**6.** Green chlorophyll is no longer produced by most plants. It breaks down and no longer masks the red and yellow pigments, which had been there all along.

**7.** In the light reactions, the sun's electromagnetic energy, which is captured by chlorophyll, breaks down water to release oxygen. Oxygen is given off as is ATP and hydrogen. In the dark reactions, the hydrogen and ATP formed in the light reactions unite with carbon dioxide to produce glucose.

### Reasoning Exercises (Page 103)

**1.** Use limited surface area to provide for the needs of all cells; transport water, minerals, and food to all parts; obtain, transport, and conserve water; coordinate all life activities of the cells; support leaves so as to obtain enough light and carbon dioxide; transfer reproductive cells on land; adapt to extreme variations in the environment.

**2.** Stomates close at night when $CO_2$ for photosynthesis is not needed.

**3.** When the light shines on the chlorophyll in the guard cells, they produce sugar. Osmosis brings water into the guard cells, which causes them to become turgid. When in this condition, the guard cells assume a curved shape. The space between two guard cells is called the stoma.

**4.** The structures of living things are adapted to their functions. Only the guard cells in the epidermis have chloroplasts; this adaptation permits the closing and opening of stomata.

## Reasoning Exercises (Page 112)

**1.** Both saprophytes and parasites take in pre-formed, high-energy food molecules.

**2.** Digestion is necessary so that food materials may pass through cell membranes.

**3.** Intracellular digestion takes place inside of cells; for example, within *Ameba.* Extracellular digestion takes place outside of cells; for example, in the stomach of humans or in the surroundings of a mold.

**4.** In *Ameba,* digestion is intracellular. In *Hydra,* digestion is both intracellular and extracellular. It is intracellular in the cells lining the digestive cavity and is extracellular in the digestive cavity.

**5.** *Hydra* has a two-way digestive system in which the mouth is used both to take in food and to egest wastes. The earthworm has special regions for various functions; the mouth and pharynx take in food, the crop stores food, the gizzard grinds food, the intestine digests food, and the anus eliminates the undigested materials.

**6.** In a one-way digestive system, various regions are specialized to perform their functions in a more efficient manner.

**7.** Although the earthworm and grasshopper differ in appearance and life-style, their digestive systems consist of the same basic pattern: a one-way tube having special compartments for storage, grinding, digestion, and absorption.

**8.** The earthworm, grasshopper, and human have a tube-within-a-tube body plan. In each case the alimentary canal is a one-way digestive system leading from mouth to anus. In the human, this canal is so lengthy that a long part of it is coiled.

## Completion Questions (Page 113)

[A] **1.** nutrients **2.** autotrophic **3.** $H_2S$ **4.** respiration **5.** the sun [B] **6.** chlorophyll **7.** chemical **8.** photosynthesis **9.** alcohol **10.** control **11.** variable **12.** reflected **13.** reds, blues **14.** magnesium **15.** grana **16.** water [C] **17.** $NADPH_2$ **18.** carbon-14 **19.** dark **20.** light **21.** ATP, $NADPH_2$ **22.** grana, stroma [D] **23.** cuticle **24.** palisade, spongy **25.** air spaces **26.** turgid **27.** transpiration **28.** guard cells [E] **29.** heterotrophic **30.** cilia **31.** mouth **32.** crop **33.** extracellular **34.** food vacuole **35.** goggles

## Multiple-Choice Questions (Page 114)

[A] **1.** (2) **2.** (1) **3.** (1) **4.** (2) [B] **5.** (1) **6.** (3) **7.** (2) **8.** (3) **9.** (1) **10.** (2) **11.** (4) **12.** (4) [C] **13.** (1) **14.** (2) **15.** (1) **16.** (1) **17.** (3) **18.** (1) **19.** (2) [D] **20.** (3) **21.** (1) **22.** (2) **23.** (3) [E] **24.** (1) **25.** (3)

## Chapter Test (Page 116)

**1.** (1) **2.** (4) **3.** (4) **4.** (A) **5.** (A) **6.** (B) **7.** (B) **8.** (A) **9.** (A) **10.** (C) **11.** (D) **12.** (4) **13.** (2) **14.** (2) **15.** (2) **16.** (2) **17.** (1) **18.** (1) **19.** (2) **20.** (4) **21.** (3) **22.** (4) **23.** (1) **24.** (2) **25.** (4) **26.** (1) **27.** (1) **28.** (3) **29.** (3) **30.** (1)

# ◼ CHAPTER 6
# TRANSPORT

## Overview

The core material explores the structure and function of the cell membrane and adaptations for transport in both plants and animals.

## Motivation

At the start of class, display a dry potted plant that has slightly drooping leaves. Pour some water on the soil and ask students what they expect to see by the end of class. Discuss with students how they think the water enters the plant from the soil and then travels upward to restore the leaves.

## Teaching Suggestions

**1.** In teaching the various theories for the upward transport of water in stems, you may need to review ideas and demonstrations from previous courses in general science. For capillary action, demonstrate a set of capillary tubes dipped into red ink. Refer also to a meniscus around a graduated cylinder. For cohesion and adhesion, point to a drop of water protruding from a faucet opening. For air pressure, use a Torricelli tube filled with mercury to show that air pressure is sufficient to hold a mercury column at a height of 76.2 cm (30 inches). Point out that this air pressure is sufficient to raise water to a height of 10.2 meters (34 feet). (***Caution:*** *Use appropriate care in handling mercury.*)

**2.** To demonstrate upward transport in stems, dip the bottom of a cut celery stalk with leaves into water colored with red ink or red food coloring. After the leaves turn red, cut across the stalk to show the colored vascular bundles.

**3.** Show the root hair on radish or bean seedlings that have been germinated on moist filter paper in petri dishes.

**4.** Perform the series of demonstrations on diffusion described on text pages 119–122.

**5.** When discussing the fluid-mosaic model and diffusion across a cell membrane, use the reproducible master of Figures 6–7 (*Transport Across A Cell Membrane*) on p. 52. Also use Chapter 6 reproducible Critical Thinking Questions 1–4 on p. 73. Ask students why active transport is shown as proceeding from the inside to the outside of the cell. As students read the chapter, encourage them to use the diagram to explain the different methods various types of molecules use to enter the cell.

**6.** From a local butcher obtain a beef heart with attached large arteries and large veins. Cut open a vein to demonstrate a valve.

# ANSWERS TO CHAPTER 6 QUESTIONS

## Reasoning Exercises (Page 125)

**1.** Although the lipid and protein molecules prevent the passage of most substances, openings within the protein molecules may serve as pores to permit other molecules to pass through.

**2.** Because water is the main transport medium, substances that are transported in an organism must first be dissolved in water.

**3.** Water osmosis is from a high concentration of its molecules to a low concentration of its molecules. If you make the solution outside of the cell more concentrated in salt, it will have a low concentration of water molecules, and water will therefore osmose to the outside.

**4.** Passive transport is diffusion through a membrane from a high concentration of a substance to a low concentration of that substance. Active transport is "wrong way" transport, against the concentration gradient, and requires the expenditure of energy. The living cell membrane is selectively permeable and keeps out some substances. Also, it uses ATP for active transport.

**5.** Pinocytosis and phagocytosis differ mainly in the size of the material taken in through the cell membrane. Pinocytosis takes in large molecules; phagocytosis takes in even larger substances, such as living microorganisms.

**6.** Absorption is a general term for the taking of materials into a cell. Circulation involves the larger process of transporting materials throughout a cell and of transporting materials to the various parts of a many-celled organism.

## Reasoning Exercises (Page 134)

**1.** Vascular pertains to ducts or vessels that convey fluids. The two main vascular tissues in an herbaceous stem are xylem and phloem.

**2.** Annual rings are formed when alternating regions of large cells and small cells are formed in the xylem during the spring and the summer, respectively.

**3.** Xylem generally carries water upward in the stem and phloem generally carries food downward.

**4.** Root hairs are protrusions from the surface of the root; thus, they increase the surface area available for absorption of water.

**5.** A scientific law describes a regularity in nature. For example, in physics the law of reflection for light states that the angle of incidence is equal to the angle of reflection. A scientific theory is an attempt to *explain* observable events and laws.

**6.** The theories that explain the upward transport of liquids in stems are (1) adhesion and cohesion, (2) capillary action, (3) root pressure, (4) atmospheric pressure, and (5) transpiration pull-cohesion tension.

## Reasoning Exercises (Page 137)

**1.** A paramecium expels excess water by active transport at the contractile vacuoles. It accumulates this excess water by osmosis from the outside. If it did not constantly expel water it would burst.

**2.** In an open circulatory system the blood at times flows through large spaces called sinuses. In a closed circulatory system, the blood always flows through tubes. The closed system circulates blood faster.

**3.** Nutrients in an earthworm's closed circulatory system diffuse into cells from the nearby thin-walled capillaries. Nutrients in the grasshopper's open circulatory system diffuse into the cells that line the sinuses and their branches.

**4.** The earthworm's blood carries oxygen and carbon dioxide; its blood contains hemoglobin (but not in red blood cells) to assist in this task. The grasshopper has a system of tracheal tubes for the transport of the respiratory gases and does not use its blood for this purpose. Its blood has no hemoglobin.

## Completion Questions (Page 137)

[A] **1.** protein molecules **2.** hypothesis, or a model
**3.** fluid-mosaic model [B] **4.** diffusion **5.** semi-permeable
**6.** plasmolysis **7.** concentration gradient **8.** pinocytosis
[C] **9.** phloem **10.** absorption **11.** cambium **12.** zone of differentiation **13.** cohesion **14.** capillary action
[D] **15.** diffusion **16.** anterior **17.** aortic arches
**18.** grasshopper **19.** skin **20.** open

## Multiple-Choice Questions (Page 138)

[A] **1.** (3) **2.** (1) **3.** (4) [B] **4.** (2) **5.** (2) **6.** (2)
**7.** (4) **8.** (3) [C] **9.** (3) **10.** (1) **11.** (3) **12.** (2) **13.** (4)
**14.** (3) **15.** (3) **16.** (4) [D] **17.** (1) **18.** (3) **19.** (4)
**20.** (2)

## Chapter Test (Page 139)

**1.** (4) **2.** (3) **3.** (1) **4.** (1) **5.** (1) **6.** (2) **7.** (1)
**8.** (3) **9.** (4) **10.** (2) **11.** (3) **12.** (3) **13.** (2)
**14.** (3) **15.** (3) **16.** F (or G) **17.** (B) **18.** (C) **19.** (E)
**20.** (D) **21.** (C) **22.** (C) **23.** (B) **24.** (D) **25.** (A)

# CHAPTER 7
# RESPIRATION

## Overview

The core material explains the chemistry of oxidation-reduction reactions and describes cellular respiration and adaptations for respiration. The extended material describes the chemistry of cellular respiration.

## Motivation

Display close-up photographs or describe a rusted automobile, a fire, and a person running. Ask students what these items have in common. Point out that in every instance oxygen is being used and energy is being released. Encourage students to speculate on how energy is released and used by a person without the destructiveness that occurs in a fire or rust. Discuss why a person may feel tired and breathless after running.

## Teaching Suggestions

1. Burn a piece of magnesium ribbon or a wood splint and compare it with respiration in a living animal. Elicit from the class a comparison such as that shown in the table on text page 143.

2. To show that the slow oxidation of iron releases heat energy, place wet steel wool in a thermos bottle. Place a thermometer inside the bottle so that it protrudes from the top of the sealed bottle. The rise in temperature will be seen by the following day. Repeat the experiment with germinating seeds in another thermos bottle. (*Caution: Steel wool may damage your thermos.*)

3. In a darkened room, luciferin and luciferase glow after ATP is added. Materials for this bioluminescent demonstration can be obtained as a kit from a biological supply house.

4. To demonstrate anaerobic respiration, display several fermentation tubes containing the following: dilute molasses and yeast, a container of yogurt, a can of sauerkraut, a bottle of cider, and a piece of yeast bread. Explain that gas is produced in the tubes. Relate this to the fermentation process that produces yogurt, sauerkraut, cider, and the rise of yeast bread dough.

5. You may wish to further demonstrate fermentation by preparing a simple dough made of sugar, water, yeast, and flour. Cover the dough and keep it warm. After the dough rises, explain what happened. Point out that without the yeast, the bread would be heavy and dense.

6. As students read the chapter, you may wish to have them complete the Chapter 7 Critical Thinking Questions, p.74. Discuss answers after students have finished.

## ANSWERS TO CHAPTER 7 QUESTIONS

### Reasoning Exercises (Page 145)

1. Photosynthesis stores radiant energy in the form of chemical energy of organic molecules, such as glucose. Respiration releases the chemical energy stored in organic molecules such as glucose. In addition, the raw materials and end products of these two processes are just the opposite.

2. See table on page 143.

3. ATP is an organic molecule consisting of adenosine and three phosphate groups. The last two phosphate groups are held by high energy bonds.

4. In the hydrolysis of ATP, ATP-ase helps to combine ATP with water to form ADP and P to release energy. In the syntheses of ATP, ATP-ase helps to combine ADP with P and energy to form ATP.

5. Oxidation is the loss of electrons or of hydrogen. When a substance combines with oxygen, it loses electrons to the oxygen atoms; accordingly, the combination of a substance with oxygen is an example of oxidation.

### Reasoning Exercises (Page 155)

1. The respiratory surfaces of both the earthworm and the human are thin, moist, close to a source of oxygen, and close to a gas-transport system.

2. The respiratory surface of the earthworm is the external skin, which permits the exchange of respiratory gases between the outside and the thin-walled blood capillaries. The respiratory surface of the human consists of the thin membranes of the alveoli (air sacs), which permit the passage of gases between the air sacs of the lungs and the thin-walled blood capillaries. The respiratory surface of the earthworm consists of the entire body surface, which must be kept moist. Since the respiratory system of the human is internal, with the exception of the nostrils, the surface of the human body is able to remain dry.

3. A fish will die when it is taken from water for an extended period of time because the respiratory surfaces of the gills must remain moist in order for oxygen to pass to the blood. If these surfaces become dry, respiration in the fish cannot function.

4. The hemoglobin, which is dissolved in the earthworm's blood, has a high capacity for carrying oxygen.

5. The grasshopper uses a system of tracheal tubes, rather than blood, to carry oxygen to the tissues.

### Completion Questions (Page 155)

[A] 1. ATP-ase 2. $CO_2$ 3. ATP 4. ADP 5. electrons, hydrogen 6. electrons, hydrogen 7. aerobes

[B] 8. mitochondria 9. carbon dioxide, alcohol 10. carbon dioxide, water 11. pyruvic acid 12. 2 ATP 13. 36 ATP 14. 20 15. 38 [C] 16. Krebs cycle 17. Krebs cycle 18. electron transport chain 19. water

**20.** diffusion **21.** dry **22.** oxygen **23.** thin, moist
**24.** lenticels **25.** cell membrane **26.** mucus
**27.** iron **28.** oxygen **29.** tracheae **30.** spiracles

## Multiple-Choice Questions (Page 156)
A **1.** (1) **2.** (3) **3.** (2) **4.** (3) B **5.** (3) **6.** (1) **7.** (4)
**8.** (1) **9.** (1) **10.** (2) **11.** (2) **12.** (2) C **13.** (1) **14.** (2)

# CHAPTER 8
# EXCRETION

## Overview
The core material describes the products of excretion and explores adaptations for excretion in protists, plants, and animals.

## Motivation
Ask students if they know what urine contains. Point out that the major part of urine is water in which wastes are dissolved for passage out of the body. Invite students to discuss what adapations they think desert animals have developed to excrete wastes without wasting water.

## Teaching Suggestions
**1.** To demonstrate that a green plant gives off carbon dioxide at night, place *Elodea* in several indicators and keep the plants in a dark cupboard. In acid conditions bromthymol blue turns yellow, phenolphthalein changes from pink to colorless, and phenol red turns yellow. Invite students to suggest needed controls, such as using a similar setup without the plants. Discuss with students the assumptions they might make from this demonstration of carbon dioxide production.

**2.** Use prepared microscope slides to demonstrate stomata and lenticels.

**3.** Demonstrate nephridia and Malpighian tubules by means of prepared microscope slides. Also point them out during lab dissections.

**4.** To show that urea has an amino component, break down urea through the action of the enzyme urease:

$$CO(NH_2)_2 \xrightarrow{\text{urease}} CO_2 + NH_3$$

Dissolve some urea in water and divide the solution into two beakers. Add bromthymol blue to each beaker. Then add a bit of urease solution to one beaker. The formation of ammonia will quickly turn the solution yellow.

**5.** Refer to Lab Skills 13 and 14 for an experiment which indicates that the enzyme urease promotes the breakdown of urea at body temperature.

**6.** After students read the chapter, you may wish to have them complete the Chapter 8 Critical Thinking Questions on p. 74. Discuss the answers.

**15.** (3) D **16.** (3) **17.** (2) E **18.** (3) **19.** (1) **20.** (1)
**21.** (1) **22.** (2) **23.** (4) **24.** (4) **25.** (1)

## Chapter Test (Page 158)
**1.** (2) **2.** (4) **3.** (1) **4.** (3) **5.** (3) **6.** (1) **7.** (4) **8.** (2)
**9.** (4) **10.** (1) **11.** (1) **12.** (3)

## ANSWERS TO CHAPTER 8 QUESTIONS

### Reasoning Exercises (Page 163)
**1.** Excretion is the removal of metabolic wastes. Defecation is the removal of undigested food. Excretion is necessary for homeostasis.
**2.** Deamination is the removal of amino groups from amino acids or proteins. Nitrogenous wastes are excreted in the form of ammonia, urea, and uric acid.
**3.** The main function of the contractile vacuole is to remove excess water.
**4.** Stomates and lenticels give off carbon dioxide. Some excretory products are sealed off in vacuoles.
**5.** Ammonia is poisonous and requires large amounts of water for it to be removed without injuring cells. As land animals possessing a limited supply of water, humans would have to expend excessive amounts of water to remove ammonia.
**6.** The earthworm possesses pairs of nephridia segmentally arranged. These pass wastes, including ammonia, urea, and mineral salts, from the body fluid to the outside. Carbon dioxide passes to the outside through the moist skin.
**7.** The Malpighian tubules of the grasshopper pick up nitrogenous wastes, mineral salts, and water from the sinuses, reabsorb most of the water, and pass dry wastes into the large intestine. The nitrogenous waste is uric acid.
**8.** The human organs of excretion include the kidneys, lungs, skin, and liver. Humans excrete urea dissolved in the urine that passes from the kidneys and in the sweat from the skin. The earthworm's nephridia resemble the human's nephrons.

### Completion Questions (Page 164)
A **1.** elimination, defecation, or egestion **2.** metabolic
**3.** excretion **4.** amino **5.** amino B **6.** diffusion
**7.** photosynthesis C **8.** nitrates **9.** vacuoles
D **10.** Malpighian tubules **11.** insoluble **12.** urea
**13.** nephridia **14.** Malpighian tubules **15.** sweat

### Multiple-Choice Questions (Page 164)
A **1.** (1) **2.** (3) **3.** (2) **4.** (3) B **5.** (2) **6.** (1) C **7.** (2)
**8.** (3) D **9.** (2) **10.** (1) **11.** (1) **12.** (2) **13.** (4) **14.** (2)

### Chapter Test (Page 166)
**1.** (4) **2.** (2) **3.** (4) **4.** (4) **5.** (4) **6.** (D) **7.** (C) **8.** (C)
**9.** (C) **10.** (B) **11.** (1) **12.** (1) **13.** (2) **14.** (3) **15.** (4)

# CHAPTER 9
# REGULATION

## Overview

Chapter 9 presents core material on nerve function, adaptation of nerve control in animals, and chemical control in plants and animals.

## Motivation

Invite students to recall trying to swat a fly or a mosquito. Discuss the number of failed attempts as compared to successful attempts. Ask students how the insect senses their approach. Then have students place their hands on the desk or table and close their eyes. Tell them you will move about the room and lightly touch students' hands at random. After touching several hands, discuss with students what sensations they felt in anticipation of being touched and any reflex pulling back of hands by those who were touched. Point out that these reactions are part of the nervous system.

## Teaching Suggestions

1. Use a microprojector to show a prepared slide of nerve tissue containing a myoneural junction. You may follow-up by asking students to answer Critical Thinking Question 5 on p. 75.

2. To observe galvanotaxis of protozoa, place a drop of a rich culture of *Paramecium* into a U-shaped tube. Shine a strong light through the tube to project the shadow of the tube and the protozoa upon a screen. Into the ends of the tube insert wires leading from two dry cells connected in a series. The protozoa will cluster near the negative electrode. You may also wish to try this activity on an overhead projector. (*Caution: Do not overheat the protozoans from prolonged exposure to the light source.*)

3. Introduce auxins by displaying a plant that has been grown in one position on a windowsill. Ask why the stem is bent. Students may explain that the stem turned toward the light because of phototropism. Ask students to explain phototropism. If students say that a tropism is a bending toward or away from a stimulus, point out the circular reasoning involved. Note that giving a name for a phenomenon does not explain it. For students who say that the plant "seeks" or "needs" the light, point out that teleological explanations are of no value to the biologist. Then examine the procedures and the reasoning historically used by biologists to investigate what makes plants turn toward the light.

4. To demonstrate examples of plant tropisms, make a "pocket garden" consisting of a blotter placed between two glass lantern slide plates. Arrange a row of radish seeds on the blotter and fasten the assembly with rubber bands. Place the garden in a vertical position in a tray of water to keep the blotter moist. After the roots have started to grow downward, rotate the garden 90 degrees. The roots will make an abrupt bend.

5. Obtain auxin dispersed in lanolin from a biological supply house. Demonstrate the action of auxins by applying the auxin to one side of a bean plant stem that has been grown in the dark. If students are confused about why an excess of growth-promoting auxin on one side of the stem should cause a bending away from that side, use the following analogy: If marchers on the left side of a marching band take small steps and those on the right side take large steps, the entire band will turn to the left. The turning is away from the side where the marchers move fastest. As a follow-up, have students answer Chapter 9 Critical Thinking Questions 7–9 on p. 75.

6. Provide students with the reproducible master of Figure 9–9 on p. 53. Ask students to describe what happens when a grasshopper is touched on its antennae, when it hears or sees someone approach. Have students use a pen or colored pencil to trace the different paths of the sensory impulses to the grasshopper's brain that will result in the grasshopper jumping away.

## ANSWERS TO CHAPTER 9 QUESTIONS

### Reasoning Exercises (Page 176)

1. Receptors receive a stimulus and initiate an impulse. Effectors are the muscles and glands that respond to impulses.

2. A neuron is a nerve cell. A nerve is a bundle of axons or dendrites.

3. A paramecium moves toward or away from stimuli. The cilia beat in a coordinated, wavelike manner.

4. The feeding reflex of *Hydra* is initiated by glutathione, a substance that is released from the tissues of the prey when pierced by the nematocysts of *Hydra*.

5. The nervous system of *Hydra* consists merely of a diffuse nerve net over which impulses can pass in any direction. The nervous system of the earthworm is more complex in that its neurons are organized into nerves, ganglia, and a central nerve cord. Impulses take a definite pathway. A large, paired ganglion serves as a brain that coordinates activities.

6. The nervous system of the grasshopper resembles that of the earthworm because it has a ventral nerve cord that is connected to the dorsal "brain" by a ring of nerve tissues that passes around the digestive system. However, the nervous system of the grasshopper is more complex; it has more fusion of ganglia, and possesses receptors in specialized organs such as the eyes, antennae, and tympanum.

7. The terminal branches of the first neuron release

neurotransmitter molecules that diffuse across the gap. There they combine with receptors on the dendrites of the second neuron and initiate an impulse in the second neuron.

**8.** In contrast to invertebrates, the nerve cord of vertebrates is dorsal to the digestive canal and is a hollow tube without segmentally arranged ganglia within it. In vertebrates, the nerve cord is expanded into a hollow enlargement called the brain.

**9.** A nerve impulse is an electro-chemical reaction caused by the flow of ions across successive points of the cell membrane.

## Reasoning Exercises (Page 181)

**1.** A tropism is the growth of part of a plant toward or away from a stimulus. A taxis is the movement of an entire organism toward or away from a stimulus.

**2.** Light destroys auxin on the near side of the stem, causing an unequal distribution of this plant hormone. Auxin on the far side of the stem causes increased growth on that side, which results in bending.

**3.** In a root growing horizontally, gravity will pull the root auxin downward, causing an unequal distribution. The auxin inhibits growth in the lower part of the root, which causes a bending downward.

**4.** Plant hormones are used to kill weeds, to stimulate root formation for cuttings, to produce seedless fruit, and to prevent the fall of fruit.

**5.** Positive hydrotropism. It enables the plant to obtain the water needed for life.

## Completion Questions (Page 183)

A 1. endocrine system **2.** impulse **3.** glands **4.** axon **5.** synapse **6.** acetylcholine, noradrenaline **7.** cholinesterase **8.** polarized **9.** impulse **10.** frequent **11.** motor (afferent) **12.** interneurons B 13. nerve net **14.** ventral **15.** irritability **16.** *Hydra* **17.** feeding **18.** cilia **19.** ganglia **20.** bilaterally **21.** dorsal **22.** dorsal **23.** hollow C 24. 2, 4-D **25.** inhibit **26.** coleoptile **27.** tropism **28.** taxis **29.** specialization **30.** right **31.** phototropism D 32. hormones **33.** nervous **34.** target **35.** endocrine gland **36.** blood **37.** endocrine, ductless **38.** exocrine or duct **39.** long **40.** juvenile hormone

## Multiple-Choice Questions (Page 184)

A 1. (4) **2.** (3) **3.** (3) **4.** (4) **5.** (4) **6.** (4) **7.** (3) **8.** (2) **9.** (1) **10.** (3) B 11. (4) **12.** (1) **13.** (2) **14.** (1) C 15. (3) **16.** (2) **17.** (4) **18.** (3) **19.** (3) D 20. (2) **21.** (3) **22.** (4) **23.** (4) **24.** (3)

## Chapter Test (Page 186)

**1.** (1) **2.** (3) **3.** (1) **4.** (4) **5.** (1) **6.** (2) **7.** (2) **8.** (3) **9.** (4) **10.** (1) **11.** (2) **12.** (2) **13.** (4) **14.** (2) **15.** (4) **16.** (4) **17.** (3) **18.** (3) **19.** (1) **20.** (2) **21.** (3) **22.** (3) **23.** (3) **24.** (2) **25.** (4) **26.** (1) **27.** (1) **28.** (3) **29.** (1) **30.** (1)

# ▮ CHAPTER 10
# LOCOMOTION

## Overview

The core material points out the advantages of an organism's ability to move from place to place, and surveys the adaptations for locomotion in representative organisms.

## Motivation

Invite students to imagine being unable to move from the places they presently sit. Discuss the problems this would present in getting food and water and in avoiding a threat. Then talk about the different ways in which animals move and their reasons for moving.

## Teaching Suggestions

**1.** Display skeletons or photographs of the skeletons of a fish, a cat, a lobster, an insect, a crab, and a human. Have students categorize them as endoskeletons or exoskeletons.

**2.** While discussing bones, muscles, and leverage, use a meter stick and fulcrum to show varying arrangements whereby a lever can multiply distance. Point out that an increase in distance per unit of time means an increase in speed. Refer students to Critical Thinking Questions 5 and 7 on p. 75.

**3.** Have students use a hand lens to observe the setae of an earthworm. Encourage them to use the microscope to observe the setae in *Tubifex* worms. Direct students to answer Critical Thinking Question 3 on p. 75.

**4.** From a local butcher, obtain the ball-and-socket joint of a cow's or lamb's leg. Display how the bones in the joint move. Also obtain a chicken foot. Move the various tendons on the foot to show extension and flexion in the joints.

**5.** You may wish to have students conduct observations of the movements of live animals. For example:

■ Place several live grasshoppers or crickets in a covered terrarium or other large glass container. Encourage students to observe their movements. Suggest that they pay special attention to the movements of the jointed legs. You may wish to assign Critical Thinking Question 5 on p. 75 as a follow-up.

■ Mark a grid on the bottom of a basin or aquarium with a grease pencil. Place a crayfish in the container and have students observe and record its movements over time.

■ For practical ideas on activities in which students

observe movements of live animals, consult *Mapping Animal Movements,* by Katharine Barrett, Lawrence Hall of Science (GEMS), University of California, Berkeley, 1987.

# ANSWERS TO CHAPTER 10 QUESTIONS

## Reasoning Exercises (Page 194)

**1.** Motile organisms can move to obtain food, seek shelter, avoid toxic wastes, and escape predators. Sessile organisms survive through other adaptations. For example, some live in shallow regions of the oceans that are so rich in food that they need not pursue it, and they can produce currents of water which bring them food. Clams have heavy shells making it unnecessary to run from most predators. Snails and barnacles close their shells to avoid loss of water.

**2.** *Ameba* has pseudopods of flowing protoplasm. *Hydra* has primitive muscle cells that it uses to inch along and somersault. The earthworm has longitudinal muscles, circular muscles, and setae for pulling and pushing itself through the earth. The grasshopper has skeletal parts that act as levers when moved by muscles.

**3.** Invertebrates, such as the grasshopper, crab, and lobster have exoskeletons. Vertebrates, such as the frog, bird and human have endoskeletons. Exoskeletons protect the muscles and internal organs within. But the exoskeleton is composed of non-living chitin which does not grow with the animal. During the period of molting the animal is unprotected. Endoskeletons composed of living bone and cartilage grow with the body and their joints are more flexible. However, the endoskeleton does not provide as much protection for internal organs as does the exoskeleton.

**4.** Skeletal muscles come in pairs that oppose each other's action. When one contracts, the other relaxes.

## Completion Questions (Page 194)

A **1.** locomotion **2.** coral **3.** motile B **4.** flagellum **5.** setae **6.** joints **7.** molting **8.** endoskeleton **9.** opposable **10.** flexor

## Multiple-Choice Questions (Page 194)

A **1.** (4) **2.** (2) **3.** (4) **4.** (4) **5.** (1) **6.** (4) **7.** (3) **8.** (4) **9.** (1) **10.** (2) **11.** (3) **12.** (1) **13.** (1) **14.** (4) **15.** (1)

## Chapter Test (Page 195)

**1.** (4) **2.** (2) **3.** (2) **4.** (1) **5.** (2) **6.** (1) **7.** (2) **8.** (4) **9.** (3) **10.** (3) **11.** (2) **12.** (4) **13.** (2) **14.** (4) **15.** (3) **16.** (2) **17.** (1) **18.** (3) **19.** (3) **20.** (3)

## Unit 2 Portfolio Project

Students may illustrate one of the following organisms with labels:

- **earthworm:** *locomotion*...setae, circular muscles, longitudinal muscles; *transport*...dorsal blood vessel, ventral blood vessel, aortic arches; *nutrition*... alimentary canal, mouth, pharynx, esophagus, crop, gizzard, intestine
- **grasshopper:** *locomotion*...first walking leg, fore wing, second walking leg, jumping leg, hind flying wing; *transport*...main blood vessel, tubular heart; *nutrition*...mouth parts, salivary glands, esophagus, crop, gizzard, digestive glands, stomach, large intestine, small intestine, rectum, anus
- **human:** *locomotion*...bones, muscels, tendons *transport*...heart, arteries, capillaries, veins; *nutrition*... tongue, salivary glands, pharynx, esophagus, stomach, liver, gall bladder, bile duct, pancreas, small intestine, large intestine, appendix, rectum, anus
- **hydra:** *locomotion... nerve cells, muscle cells;* nutrition... mouth, tentacles, flagellated cell, nematocysts, gland cell

# UNIT THREE
# HUMAN PHYSIOLOGY

Unit Three provides a more detailed examination of the basic maintenance functions of nutrition, transport, respiration, excretion, regulation, and locomotion in humans.

# CHAPTER 11
# NUTRITION IN HUMANS

## Overview

The core material examines the various nutrients and their uses. The chapter describes the human nutrition system and several malfunctions. Nutrient tests and food additives are also explored.

## Motivation

Ask students what nutrition means to them. Invite them to name some of the wide variety of foods available to people in the United States. Discuss what students think is a healthy diet versus unnecessary foods people eat.

## Teaching Suggestions

**1.** Give each student an unsalted soda cracker. Direct students to chew and moisten their crackers with saliva for one minute without swallowing. Tell them to pay close attention to how the taste of the cracker may change. At the end of the minute, some students may mention that the cracker tastes sweeter. Point out that enzymes in their saliva begin digestion by breaking down the starch in the cracker into sugars.

**2.** Point out the difference between the "large" *Calorie* used by nutritionists and the "small" *calorie* used by physicists. You may wish to demonstrate the principle of the calorimeter by placing a beaker of water over a burning candle made of fat. Measure the temperature of the water before and after heating. Elicit from the class ideas about the instrumental errors in this procedure and how these errors could be corrected.

**3.** Dramatize the length of the small intestine by pacing off 23 to 25 feet in the classroom.

**4.** Encourage students to keep a food diary for three to five days. As extensions, you may wish to suggest that students weigh everything they eat on a diet scale. Refer to a nutrition handbook to estimate how many calories they are taking in, and record the type of vitamins taken in (see chart on text page 203).

**5.** Have students bring in the nutrition information panel from a box of cereal or other packaged food. Provide students with approximate caloric equivalencies for a gram of protein, of carbohydrates, and of fat (see text page 205). Have students weigh a portion of cereal, then calculate the calories it contains.

**6.** Students may also be interested in collecting food labels to note types of food additives. Suggest that students prepare a chart of common food additives and the names of foods in which these additives appear.

**7.** Discuss why there are print and television ads for stomach antacids. Ask students why the stomach is acid. Lead students to the understanding that the protein-digesting enzymes secreted by the stomach need an acid environment to function. As a follow-up, refer students back to the graph in Chapter 4 on text page 80 (Figure 4–30). Have students discuss and interpret the information shown by the graph.

**8.** When testing for nutrients, refer to the laboratory skill, textbook pp. 198–199 in Chapter 11 and Lab Skill 8 in the Appendix. The nitric-acid test is known as the xanthroproteic reaction. The test utilizing copper sulfate and potassium hydroxide is the Biuret reaction. (Sodium hydroxide may be substituted for potassium hydroxide.) You may wish to perform a demonstration by adding an equal volume of 10% sodium hydroxide to about 5 ml of fresh egg white in a test tube. Mix by shaking. Add a 0.5% copper sulfate solution, drop by drop, shaking the tube after the addition of each drop. Look for the appearance of a violet or pink-violet color. (*Caution: Use appropriate safety measures in handling acids and bases.*)

## ANSWERS TO CHAPTER 11 QUESTIONS

### Reasoning Exercises (Page 199)

**1.** Nutrients are the usable portions of foods. They are used for energy, for growth and repair, and for regulation of body processes.

**2.** See chart on page 200.

**3.** Nutrition can include aspects of ingestion, digestion, absorption, utilization, and egestion. It also includes the wise selection of food.

**4.** Waste in food, called roughage, provides fibrous bulk for peristalsis and digestion.

**5.** Calcium and phosphorus provide strength to bones and teeth. Iodine is used to manufacture thyroxine. Iron is used to manufacture hemoglobin.

**6.** Proteins, carbohydrates other than monosaccharides, and fats require digestion because their molecules are too large to pass through cell membranes.

### Reasoning Exercises (Page 209)

**1.** Mechanical digestion cuts large chunks of food into smaller chunks. This action increases the surface area of the food in preparation for chemical digestion.

Chemical digestion operates on the level of the molecule. It breaks down large molecules that cannot pass through cell membranes into smaller molecules that can pass through cell membranes.

**2.** Food is moved through the digestive tract by waves of muscle contraction called peristalsis. This will occur even if you are standing on your head.

**3.** The stomach is where food is churned and where protein digestion begins. Hydrochloric acid, produced by the gastric glands, changes the enzyme pepsinogen to its active form, pepsin—which acts on proteins. The hydrochloric acid also helps to digest minerals.

**4.** The small intestine is the region where the digestion and absorption of food occurs. In the large intestine, extra water that has been passed into the alimentary canal during digestion is reabsorbed back into the blood.

**5.** Mucus lubricates and protects the delicate lining of the alimentary canal so that it is not irritated by rough food or attacked by digestive juices.

## ▮ CHAPTER 12
## ▮ TRANSPORT IN HUMANS

### Overview
In Chapter 12, the core material explores blood as a transport medium; the protective functions of blood in blood clotting, the immune response, and allergies; and blood vessels and the heart. The extended material describes the pathway of circulation and malfunctions of the circulatory system.

### Motivation
Ask students to guess the blood volume of the human body. (A 150-pound male has about 5.5 liters of blood; a 120-pound female has about 4 liters.) Display newspaper and magazine articles about AIDS and other immune diseases. Invite students to describe how their immune system protects them and where they would find this system in the body.

### Teaching Suggestions
**1.** From a biological supply house, obtain prepared microscope slides that show the different types of cells in the blood. Include white cells stained to show their features, red cells, and platelets if possible. Set up a display for students to view and discuss these cells.

**2.** If available, show a model or a photograph of a model of the hemoglobin molecule. Point out the part of the molecule that binds to oxygen for transport in the bloodstream. Review with students what they learned about this chemical action in Chapter 4. Explain that they will be learning more about hemoglobin disorders, such as sickle cell anemia, in the upcoming chapters on

### Completion Questions (Page 211)
[A] **1.** nutrients **2.** hydrolysis **3.** fats **4.** nutrients
[B] **5.** additives **6.** calories **7.** starch **8.** glycogen
**9.** essential **10.** hydrogen **11.** saturated
[C] **12.** mouth **13.** mucus **14.** stomach **15.** peristalsis
**16.** storage **17.** feces **18.** emulsification **19.** pancreas
**20.** small intestine  [D] **21.** constipation **22.** diarrhea
**23.** ulcer **24.** cholesterol **25.** laxative

### Multiple-Choice Questions (Page 212)
[A] **1.** (4) **2.** (1) **3.** (4) **4.** (2) **5.** (1)  [B] **6.** (2) **7.** (3)
**8.** (1) **9.** (3) **10.** (1) **11.** (2) **12.** (1) **13.** (2) **14.** (2)
[C] **15.** (1) **16.** (1) **17.** (1) **18.** (4) **19.** (1) **20.** (4)
**21.** (3) **22.** (1) **23.** (2) **24.** (2) **25.** (4)

### Chapter Test (Page 213)
**1.** (2) **2.** (1) **3.** (2) **4.** (2) **5.** (3) **6.** (4) **7.** (4) **8.** (4)
**9.** (2) **10.** (3) **11.** (1) **12.** (3) **13.** (1) **14.** (1) **15.** (3)
**16.** (2) **17.** (2) **18.** (2) **19.** (2) **20.** (4) **21.** (2) **22.** (4)
**23.** (1) **24.** (1) **25.** (3)

genetics (Chapters 21 and 22).

**3.** Bring in a stethoscope and invite students to listen to each other's heartbeats. If a stethoscope is not available, have students take one another's pulse and figure out how many times the heart is beating per minute. Provide students with copies of Figures 12–5 and 12–7 from the reproducible master on p. 55. Discuss the flow of blood through the heart as demonstrated by the heartbeats.

**4.** Bring in a blood pressure cuff to show how blood pressure is taken, or ask the school nurse to do a demonstration. Explain to students how the heart creates blood pressure.

**5.** Invite a technician or medical technologist from a local blood bank to talk to the class about what blood banks do to screen blood for diseases such as HIV and hepatitis. Emphasize that people cannot contract these diseases by donating blood. If a speaker is not available, a blood bank will probably have literature on these topics for students to read.

**6.** You may want to invite a cardiologist to talk to students about the human heart and some of the heart disease problems in the United States. Ask your visitor to explain some of the possible solutions to these problems, including drug therapy, bypass operations, and angioplasty techniques.

**7.** To show students how the immune system operates, you may wish to utilize "Our Immune System: The Wars Within," by Peter Jaret, *National Geographic*, June 1986. The article contains several electron microscope photographs illustrating immune cells in action.

## ANSWERS TO CHAPTER 12 QUESTIONS

### Reasoning Exercises (Page 217)
**1.** See chart on page 216.
**2.** White blood cells engulf bacteria by process of phagocytosis.
**3.** Lymph nodes contain masses of white blood cells which destroy bacteria.

### Reasoning Exercises (Page 228)
**1.** The atria, which pump blood only a short distance to the ventricles, have thin walls. The ventricles, which pump blood through much resistance over longer distances, have thicker walls.
**2.** Arteries contain elastic tissue that expands as the arteries accept squirts of blood from the heart and muscle tissue that pumps blood. Nerve endings in arteries regulate their ability to open and close in order to control the flow of blood to a tissue or organ. Veins possess valves that permit blood to flow only toward the heart.
**3.** Lymph is mainly blood plasma that has filtered out of the capillaries into the spaces surrounding the cells. Its composition is variable but it possesses about half the protein concentrations of plasma. Lymph contains white blood cells, but plasma, being the liquid portion of the blood, has neither red blood cells, white blood cells, nor platelets.
**4.** The systolic pressure is the blood pressure that results from contraction of the left ventricle.
**5.** The red blood cells carry oxygen and carbon dioxide; the white blood cells engulf bacteria and produce antibodies; the platelets assist in blood clotting.
**6.** The lymphatic system maintains the volume of circulating blood; picks up fats which are later returned to the blood; protects the body against germs and other foreign materials.

### Completion Questions (Page 233)
A **1.** plasma **2.** hemoglobin **3.** ICF **4.** platelets
B **5.** fibrinogen **6.** platelets **7.** antigen **8.** active
**9.** interferon **10.** histamine **11.** AB **12.** negative, positive **13.** blood cells **14.** passive  C **15.** capillaries
**16.** veins **17.** skeletal muscle  D **18.** right ventricle
**19.** aorta **20.** decreases **21.** pulmonary **22.** coronary
E **23.** heart attack **24.** anemia **25.** arteriosclerosis

### Multiple-Choice Questions (Page 234)
A **1.** (3) **2.** (2) **3.** (1)  B **4.** (3) **5.** (1) **6.** (1) **7.** (1)
**8.** (2) **9.** (1) **10.** (3)  C **11.** (2) **12.** (1) **13.** (2) D **14.** (3)
**15.** (4) **16.** (1) **17.** (4)  E **18.** (2) **19.** (4) **20.** (1)

### Chapter Test (Page 235)
**1.** (3) **2.** (3) **3.** (2) **4.** (1) **5.** (2) **6.** (2) **7.** (4) **8.** (3)
**9.** (3) **10.** (2) **11.** (3) **12.** (2) **13.** (1) **14.** (2) **15.** (2)
**16.** (1) **17.** (3) **18.** (2) **19.** (3) **20.** (3) **21.** (2) **22.** (2)
**23.** (1) **24.** (1) **25.** (3)

# CHAPTER 13
# RESPIRATION IN HUMANS

## Overview
The core material explores the structure and function of the human respiratory system and the mechanisms of gas exchange. The extended material describes malfunctions of the respiratory system.

## Motivation
Invite students to place their hands on their sides and inhale and exhale deeply. Have them notice the movement of their diaphragm. Ask students why they might begin to feel dizzy if they continue to breathe so deeply. Then encourage them to recall how they felt after running or hard exercise. Call on volunteers to suggest why they had to breathe quickly and deeply for awhile.

## Teaching Suggestions
**1.** As an extension of the Motivation, invite students to spend a few minutes doing some physical activity, such as jogging in place. Before and after the activity,

have them measure their pulse, on their wrist or throat, for 15 seconds. Discuss how exercise increases the body's demand for oxygen.

**2.** Distribute copies of Figure 13–1, from the reproducible master *Human Respiratory System* on p. 56. Again invite students to inhale deeply through the nose. Have them trace on the diagram the pathway air takes to reach the lungs. Encourage them to draw an arrow to show the motion of the diaphragm. Then have students exhale, trace the pathway air takes out of the body, and draw a second arrow to show the diaphragm's motion. Discuss what happens to oxygen when it reaches the air sacs and how the body rids itself of carbon dioxide.

**3.** Exhale onto a cold pocket mirror, a piece of cold glass, or the chalkboard to demonstrate that water is produced during the process of respiration. Quickly pass a candle flame or a Bunsen burner across the chalkboard to demonstrate that water is also formed during this type of oxidation.

**4.** Obtain a beef lung from a local butcher. Cut it open and display it for students. Insert plastic tubing into one of the cartilage-lined bronchial tubes and inflate a portion of the lung by blowing into the tubing.

**5.** Arrange two bottles of water, stoppers, and glass tubing so that you can inhale air through one bottle of water and exhale through the other. Add limewater or bromthymol blue to the water in the bottles. Then demonstrate that exhaled air contains more carbon dioxide than inhaled air.

**6.** Demonstrate the bell jar model of breathing action described on text page 240. Ask students to refer to their texts as you discuss the demonstration and Critical Thinking Questions 7 and 8 on p. 78.

## ■ CHAPTER 14
## ■ EXCRETION IN HUMANS

### Overview
The core material explains the structure of the urinary system and the functions of its parts, including the roles of the lungs, skin, and liver in excretion. The extended material covers malfunctions of the excretory system.

### Motivation
Encourage students to recall a time when they were exercising or doing physical work. Ask them if they experienced a stinging sensation when sweat ran into their eyes or if they tasted salt in their mouth. Invite students to suggest reasons for these sensations. Then ask students to name other ways the body rids itself of waste. Discuss what students think might happen to the body if it was unable to rid itself of waste.

## ANSWERS TO CHAPTER 13 QUESTIONS

### Reasoning Exercises (Page 242)
**1.** During swallowing, the top of the trachea rises against the epiglottis to prevent food from entering the trachea and to divert the food into the esophagus. If the epiglottis does not function properly food might enter the trachea and cause choking.
**2.** Cigarette smoke and other particulate matter slows and then stops the beating of the cilia, which line the nasal passages and trachea. The cilia can no longer beat germs and other particles back up into the mouth to be expelled.
**3.** If you voluntarily hold your breath the carbon dioxide content of the blood increases and this stimulates the respiratory center of the medulla to cause breathing in an involuntary manner.

### Completion Questions (Page 243)
[A] **1.** pharynx **2.** bronchi **3.** alveoli **4.** epiglottis **5.** cilia **6.** diaphragm **7.** cartilage [B] **8.** internal **9.** bicarbonate ion **10.** oxyhemoglobin **11.** carbon dioxide ©  **12.** emphysema **13.** bronchitis **14.** asthma **15.** virus

### Multiple-Choice Questions (Page 243)
[A] **1.** (2) **2.** (4) **3.** (3) **4.** (4) [B] **5.** (2) **6.** (4) **7.** (2) **8.** (2) © **9.** (3) **10.** (2)

### Chapter Test (Page 244)
**1.** (1) **2.** (2) **3.** (4) **4.** (1) **5.** (1) **6.** (4) **7.** (3) **8.** (3) **9.** (1) **10.** (2)

### Teaching Suggestions
**1.** Display models of the human excretory system. Encourage students to sketch a model and label the parts. Discuss the function of each part.
**2.** Provide students with copies of Figures 14–2 and 14–3 from the reproducible masters *Human Excretory System: Kidney* and *Human Excretory System: Nephron* on pp. 57–58. Have students complete Critical Thinking Question 3 on p. 79 as they read the chapter.
**3.** Dissect fresh kidneys obtained from your local butcher or supermarket. Tease out collecting tubules to show students how many there are. Then isolate some of the tubules and place them under a dissecting microscope for students to view.
**4.** Use a microprojector to display a prepared slide of the renal corpuscles of a mammalian kidney.

**5.** Assign Critical Thinking Questions 4 and 5 on p. 79.

**6.** To demonstrate the cooling action of sweat, use a cotton ball to swab a streak of water across the chalkboard. Invite students to note the evaporation. Then swab water on the arms of student volunteers. Encourage them to describe how the evaporating water feels. Discuss evaporation of sweat as a cooling process. Ask students to suggest why they should avoid drafts after strenuous exercise.

## ANSWERS TO CHAPTER 14 QUESTIONS

### Reasoning Exercises (Page 250)

**1.** Ammonia is poisonous and requires large amounts of water for it to be removed without injuring cells. As land animals possessing a limited supply of water, humans would have to expend excessive amounts of water to remove ammonia.

**2.** The human organs of excretion include the kidneys, lungs, skin, and liver. Humans excrete urea dissolved in the urine that passes from the kidneys and also in sweat from the skin.

**3.** The body would lose water, and digested foods such as amino acids, glucose, and salts.

**4.** The skin maintains a stable body temperature in several ways. It produces sweat whose evaporation is a cooling process. Blood in skin capillaries lose heat to the outside, a process which is regulated by altering the depth at which the blood flows in small blood vessels.

**5.** If metabolic wastes are not removed from the blood they may poison cells by interfering with enzyme action.

### Completion Questions (Page 250)

Ⓐ **1.** nephrons **2.** ureters **3.** nephron **4.** urethra **5.** Bowman's Capsules **6.** glomerulus **7.** filtration, reabsorption Ⓑ **8.** sweat **9.** amino acids, urea **10.** sweat glands and kidneys **11.** dermis **12.** $CO_2$ and $H_2O$ **13.** evaporation Ⓒ **14.** uric acid **15.** lead, mercury

### Multiple-Choice Questions (Page 251)

Ⓐ **1.** (1) **2.** (1) **3.** (3) **4.** (3) **5.** (2) **6.** (4) Ⓑ **7.** (1) **8.** (3) **9.** (2) **10.** (1) Ⓒ **11.** (2) **12.** (4)

### Chapter Test (Page 252)

**1.** (3) **2.** (3) **3.** (2) **4.** (6) **5.** (5) **6.** (2) **7.** (3) **8.** (4) **9.** (2) **10.** (9)

## ■ CHAPTER 15
## REGULATION IN HUMANS

### Overview

The core material describes the structure and function of the central nervous system. The extended material covers the peripheral nervous system, the malfunctions of the nervous system, and the function of various endocrine glands.

### Motivation

Invite students to sit quietly and concentrate on the signals their bodies are receiving from the outside environment. Encourage students to note sounds and smells, the temperature of the room, the sensation of clothing and of holding a pen, the feel of the desk and chair, the amount of light in the room, and so on. Point out that people do not normally notice these things in familiar surroundings, unless something new is introduced. Explain that even when people are unaware of their surroundings, the nervous system is constantly receiving information from the environment and sending it to the brain for processing.

### Teaching Suggestions

**1.** Demonstrate the blinking reflex by having a student hold a sheet of clear plastic in front of and near the face. (*Caution: Do not use glass. Make sure the plastic is sturdy and unbreakable.*) Wave your hand in front of the plastic. The subject should blink involuntarily. You could also toss small wads of paper at the plastic and have students observe the subject's blinking reflex. Point out the involuntary, unlearned nature of this behavior.

**2.** Invite students to team up with a partner to participate in an activity on the pupillary reflex. Direct one partner to face the light from a window or ceiling light with eyes closed. The second partner observes what happens to the other partner's pupils when the eyes are opened.

**3.** As you discuss the different parts of the nervous system, have students complete Critical Thinking Questions 1–5 on p. 80.

**4.** To demonstrate how an insulin deficiency might be determined, perform glucose tests on samples of urine, some of which have been "doctored" with concentrations of glucose. Use Benedict's solution, Clinitest tablets, or Clinistix strips to test the samples. A substitute for real urine may be prepared by using water colored with potassium dichromate or organic dyes to which glucose has been added.

**5.** Display a vial of adrenaline. Discuss the conditions under which a physician might administer this hormone during an emergency. In the discussion, highlight the positive effects of this hormone that make it so useful in emergencies. You may also wish to discuss the negative effects of adrenaline in people who are under a great deal of stress.

**6.** While discussing the human endocrine system, you may wish to have students complete and discuss Critical Thinking Questions 6–12 on p. 80.

## ANSWERS TO CHAPTER 15 QUESTIONS

### Reasoning Exercises (Page 260)
1. See table on page 253.
2. The cerebrum is involved in studying for a test. The cerebellum is involved in walking a tightrope.
3. The heat is the stimulus which affects the dendrites of a sensory neuron. The dendrites are the receptors. The impulse passes over the sensory neuron to the spinal cord where a synapse is made first with an interneuron and then with a motor neuron. The motor neuron carries an impulse to a muscle in the hand, which acts as an effector and contracts.
4. Sympathetic nerves release adrenaline (or noradrenaline), which inhibits visceral muscle in the digestive system. Parasympathetic nerves release acetylcholine, which stimulates visceral muscle in the digestive system.

### Reasoning Exercises (Page 269)
1. A hormone is the secretion of an endocrine gland.
2. The growth hormone of the anterior pituitary gland increases the size of the body by promoting the growth of long bones. Thyroxin, produced by the thyroid gland, increases the general rate of the body's metabolism. Adrenaline, produced by the adrenal medulla, reinforces the effects of the sympathetic nervous system by such effects as increasing the rate and strength of the heartbeat, stimulating respiration, and changing glycogen to glucose.
3. The hypothalamus is part of the brain and the pituitary gland is part of the endocrine system. Yet the hypothalamus produces hormones that move to the pituitary gland via blood capillaries or via nerve fibers.

The hormones are stored in the pituitary gland until released.
4. Diabetes mellitus is a hyperglycemia resulting, in children, from a lack of insulin. A goiter is a swelling of the thyroid gland in the neck. One form of goiter is associated with a lack of thyroxin production, or hypothyroidism. This is sometimes caused by a lack of iodine in the diet.
5. The anterior pituitary gland secretes ACTH which stimulates the adrenal cortex to release cortisol. An excess of cortisol in the blood, however, shuts off the pituitary gland's release of ACTH and thus lowers the amount of cortisol in the blood.

### Completion Questions (Page 269)
A 1. peripheral 2. cerebellum 3. cerebrum 4. spinal canal 5. meninges 6. medulla 7. interneurons 8. habits B 9. mixed 10. autonomic 11. sympathetic 12. acetylcholine 13. peripheral C 14. movement 15. meningitis 16. motor 17. anterior poliomyelitis D 18. anterior pituitary 19. goiter 20. thyroid 21. hypothalamus 22. insulin 23. follicle stimulating hormone 24. insulin 25. negative feedback 26. endorphins, enkephalins.

### Multiple-Choice Questions (Page 270)
A 1. (3) 2. (1) 3. (3) 4. (2) 5. (2) B 6. (1) 7. (1) 8. (2) 9. (4) C 10. (1) 11. (1) D 12. (2) 13. (1) 14. (4) 15. (1) 16. (3) 17. (4) 18. (4) 19. (3) 20. (2) 21. (3) 22. (1)

### Chapter Test (Page 272)
1. (1) 2. (4) 3. (1) 4. (1) 5. (2) 6. (1, 2, 4) 7. (4) 8. (1) 9. (4) 10. (2) 11. (2) 12. (3) 13. (1) 14. (3) 15. (2)

# CHAPTER 16
# LOCOMOTION IN HUMANS

## Overview
The core material explores locomotion in humans by describing the human skeleton, muscles, and connective tissues. The extended material describes some malfunctions associated with locomotion.

## Motivation
Invite two students to walk around the room. Discuss which bodily structure keeps them upright and which structure creates the movement. Then encourage students to raise and bend their arms. Discuss the muscles that produce each movement and the connective tissue that allows the arm to bend. Invite students to recall times when their muscles have felt stiff after unaccustomed exercise. Ask them to suggest reasons for this stiffness.

## Teaching Suggestions
1. If possible, display a full-size human skeleton or a model. Demonstrate how the bones are articulated by moving an arm or leg. Provide students with copies of Figure 16–2 from the reproducible master *Human Skeleton*. Have them name and point out the different parts of the skeleton. Then have students answer the Critical Thinking Questions on p. 81.

2. Try to obtain from your local butcher an animal's leg bone with muscle attached. Also obtain a heart and a section of the intestines. Display these items and have students note how the muscle is attached to the leg bone. Encourage them to compare the different types of muscle tissue found in the leg, the heart, and the intestines.

3. Conduct a laboratory session devoted to an examination of prepared slides of cartilage, bone, muscle, and connective tissue.

4. If film or video equipment is available, show students a film of ballet dancers and/or athletes competing in track events. Try to select a film that

shows some action in slow motion. Encourage students to observe and discuss the muscular development needed to create the wide range of movements these people perform.

**5.** Obtain from a local butcher a ball-and-socket joint, or use a joint on the human skeleton model. Demonstrate the movement for students. Then have them complete Critical Thinking Question 2 on p. 81.

**6.** Invite students to make observations of the variable stride length in humans. Lay down lengths of rolled brown wrapping paper, or have students perform this activity on a linoleum floor. Dampen each student's shoes and have him or her take several normal walking steps. Have other students measure the stride length between the footsteps. Then encourage students to create a graph that plots stride length on the x-axis versus number of individuals on the y-axis. Choose intervals on each axis carefully, so that the graph will show a frequency distribution of several categories of stride length for the students in the class.

## ANSWERS TO CHAPTER 16 QUESTIONS

### Reasoning Exercises (Page 278)

**1.** Both the grasshopper and the human have a skeleton whose parts are used as levers to increase speed. However, the grasshopper has an exoskeleton composed of non-living chitin and the human has an endoskeleton composed of living bone and cartilage.

**2.** The functions of bones include: support and protection of body structures, anchorage sites for muscle action, leverage for body movements, and production of blood cells in the marrow.

**3.** The functions of cartilage include: pliable support, flexibility of joints, and cushioning effects in joints.

**4.** Three types of muscle in the human body are: visceral muscle, which is involuntary in action and smooth in appearance; cardiac muscle, which is involuntary in action and striated in appearance; and skeletal muscle, which is voluntary in action and striated in appearance.

**5.** Both tendons and ligaments are types of connective tissue. Tendons are tough, inelastic, fibrous cords that attach muscles to bones. Ligaments connect bones to bones at movable joints.

### Completion Questions (Page 278)

Ⓐ **1.** calcium phosphate **2.** opposable **3.** ligament **4.** pectoral **5.** skeletal **6.** tendon **7.** flexor **8.** extensor **9.** skeletal **10.** visceral **11.** spinal cord **12.** matrix
Ⓑ **13.** arthritis **14.** tendonitis

### Multiple-Choice Questions (Page 279)

Ⓐ **1.** (1) **2.** (3) **3.** (1) **4.** (4) **5.** (3) **6.** (4) **7.** (3)
Ⓑ **8.** (4) **9.** (3) **10.** (3)

### Chapter Test (Page 279)

**1.** (3) **2.** (2) **3.** (4) **4.** (1) **5.** (4) **6.** (2) **7.** (3) **8.** (2) **9.** (3) **10.** (1) **11.** (3) **12.** (4) **13.** (1) **14.** (1) **15.** (3)

**Unit 3 Portfolio Projects**

1. Answers will vary. Photos of running, jumping, and skating or skiing athletes should be accompanied by descriptions of the motions of the pelvic girdle, femur, tibia, fibula, knee joint, ankle joint, and foot bones in motion. To the extent that a photo shows arm motion, a description of motions in the pectoral girdle, humerus, radius, ulna, and elbow joint may also be included. Photos of athletes throwing or swinging a bat, tennis racket, golf club, hockey stick, or any other object should be accompanied by descriptions of the pectoral girdle, humerus, radius, ulna, elbow joint, wrist joint, and bones of the hand in motion. Descriptions of motions in the spine, pelvic girdle, or leg bones may also be included if the photo shows movements of these body parts. Photos of swimming and diving athletes should be accompanied by descriptions of motions of bones in all four limbs.

2. Digestion in the Mouth: Ingredients with starch should be listed in this column because salivary amylase begins digestion of starch. Digestion in the Stomach: Ingredients with protein should be listed in this column because pepsin, a protease formed in the stomach, begins digestion of protein. Digestion in the Small Intestine: Ingredients with fat should be listed in this column because bile secretions and lipases are present in this organ. Ingredients with sugars (disaccharides such as sucrose, lactose, or maltose) should be listed in this column. Ingredients with protein or starch may also be listed in this column because proteases and amylases are part of the pancreatic secretions into the small intestine, where the digestion of these nutrients is completed.

# UNIT FOUR
# REPRODUCTION AND DEVELOPMENT

Unit Four presents asexual and sexual reproduction and development in plants and animals. Mitosis, meiosis, and fertilization are introduced, and the development of plant and animal embryos are explained. Hormonal interactions in the human male and female are also covered.

# CHAPTER 17
# ASEXUAL REPRODUCTION

## Overview
Chapter 17 covers the cell cycle, mitosis, and methods of asexual reproduction in single-celled and multi-celled organisms.

## Motivation
Invite students to suggest the average healing time for a small cut or surface burn on a hand. Encourage them to describe what they think is happening on the cellular level to produce new skin at the site of the cut or burn. Then point to a potted plant and discuss whether the same type of new cell production occurs in plants. Ask students how this process might be utilized to create new and separate plants.

## Teaching Suggestions
1. In teaching mitosis, use charts and models freely and provide laboratory microscope work. You may also wish to show one of several available films or film loops taken by phase-contrast microscopy that presents mitosis as a continuous process.

2. When discussing the process of mitosis, suggest that students sketch the process for themselves. Provide students with copies of Figures 17–6 through 17–10 from the reproducible masters on pp. 60–61.

3. You may also wish to have students construct models that show chromosomes during mitosis, using materials such as pop-it beads and pipe cleaners.

4. To help students understand asexual reproduction, display examples of vegetative propagation, such as an onion bulb, a potato tuber, runners from strawberry plants or from garden weeds, and iris rhizomes. Suggest that students complete Critical Thinking Question 10.

5. Bring to class a potted geranium plant. Make a cutting and plant it in a second pot. Invite students to observe the plant's growth over several weeks. Also encourage them to make their own cuttings or to propagate new plants from potatoes or onions.

6. If living *Hydra* are available, you may wish to use a microprojector to display any specimens that are budding.

## ANSWERS TO CHAPTER 17 QUESTIONS

### Reasoning Exercises (Page 287)
1. Reproduction maintains the life of the species rather than the life of the individual.

2. Sexual reproduction involves the fusion of two gametes, but asexual reproduction involves only one parent.

3. Cell division includes mitosis and cytoplasmic division.

4. Accept responses that show comprehension of pp. 284–286 in the textbook.

5. When mitosis begins, each chromosome is doubled, i.e., it contains two chromatids, each of which is identical to its partner. It is the replication of DNA that makes the doubled chromosomes.

6. The doubled chromosomes separate into single chromosomes during anaphase.

7. Plant cells carry on mitosis without having centrioles. Cytoplasmic division is accomplished by formation of a cell plate rather than by a pinching of the cell in two.

8. As a result of mitotic cell division, the chromosome number is maintained. Each daughter cell receives a replica of all the chromosomes in the parent cell, and the same volume of protoplasm now has more surface area.

### Reasoning Exercises (Page 294)
1. Offspring produced by asexual means have the same heredity as their parents because all cells are formed by mitosis, a process that conserves the original chromosome makeup of cells.

2. Five advantages of vegetative propagation are:
• No variations in traits • speed of growth • certainty of growth • seedless fruits • desirable characteristics of different plant varieties combined in one plant.

### Completion Questions (Page 294)
Ⓐ 1. two 2. interphase, mitosis 3. spindle
4. replication [B] 5. centromere 6. eight 7. cell membrane 8. cell plate [C] 9. asexual 10. spore formation 11. regeneration 12. vegetative propagation 13. rhizomes 14. buds 15. stock 16. scion

### Multiple-Choice Questions (Page 294)
Ⓐ 1. (2) 2. (3) 3. (3) 4. (3) [B] 5. (3) 6. (1) 7. (3)
8. (4) 9. (2) 10. (3) 11. (1) [C] 12. (1) 13. (1)
14. (3) 15. (2) 16. (1) 17. (3)

### Chapter Test (Page 295)
1. (4) 2. (2) 3. (2) 4. (2) 5. (1) 6. (1) 7. (3) 8. (1)
9. (3) 10. (2)

# CHAPTER 18
# SEXUAL REPRODUCTION IN ANIMALS

## Overview

The core material presents conjugation and fertilization in animals and explains meiosis in cells. The extended material explores the development of embryos and reproduction and development in humans.

## Motivation

Recall with students that vegetative propagation produces exact copies of parent plants because reproduction is asexual. Discuss with students what constitutes the variety in offspring produced by sexual reproduction in plants and animals.

## Teaching Suggestions

1. Encourage students to make models showing the main steps of meiosis. Suggest they use pop-it beads and pipe cleaners. Recommend that different colored pipe cleaners be used to show each pair of homologous chromosomes. Discuss with students how the models of meiosis help them to understand the difference between meiosis and mitosis.

2. Provide students with copies of Figure 18–3 from the reproducible master on p. 62. Suggest they use the diagram of meiosis to help them complete and discuss Critical Thinking Questions 1–6 on the master.

3. Use prepared microscope slides to show the cleavage in the sea urchin egg. Follow this presentation with a series of models on early embryo development

4. Some biological supply companies or chicken farms will supply a series of fertilized eggs, with eggs that are five, seven, and nine days old. Open one egg from each stage to allow the class to view a chick's development.

5. Use dissected specimens, museum preparations, models, and charts to show the location and appearance of the gonads in fish, frogs, chickens, and rats.

6. Demonstrate gastrulation by indenting balls of clay. You may wish to have students complete Critical Thinking Question 7 on p. 82.

7. You may wish to have students mark the answers to Critical Thinking Questions 8–12 on pp. 64–65, *Human Reproductive System: Male* and *Human Reproductive System: Female.* Students can number each structure on the diagram with the question number it answers.

8. Distribute copies of Figure 18–10, *Human Fetus and Placenta,* when discussing the development of the human embryo. Point out that chorionic villi sampling can be done earlier than amniocentesis, which is generally performed in the fifteenth to seventeenth week of pregnancy.

## ANSWERS TO CHAPTER 18 QUESTIONS

### Reasoning Exercises (Page 303)

1. Sexual reproduction increases the variability of the offspring and may permit the species to adapt to a changing environment.

2. Sperm are much smaller than ova. Sperm swim by means of flagellar locomotion; ova are not motile. In many vertebrate animals, the ovum contains yolk. Sperm, by comparison, have much less stored energy than do ova. Sperm are also produced in far greater numbers.

3. From one primary sex cell, oogenesis produces an ovum and three polar bodies. Spermatogenesis produces four sperm cells.

4. A hermaphrodite produces both sperm cells and egg cells.

5. Meiosis and fertilization together maintain the chromosome number from generation to generation. Without meiosis, fusion of gametes during fertilization would increase the chromosome number from generation to generation. As a result of meiosis, gametes have half the chromosome number of the species.

6. The diploid number is 14.

7. Crossing-over rearranges genes on the chromosomes. In a population of reproducing individuals, this rearrangement increases overall variability of gametes and offspring. For example, crossing-over establishes new linkages while breaking up existing ones. The genetic variability produced by crossing-over gives the species more variable traits. These, in turn, make the species better equipped to adapt to new environments, or to changing ones.

8. Conjugation in protists is the exchange of nuclear material between two individuals. It occurs in species whose primary mode of reproduction is asexual. Conjugation in bacteria involves the exchange of chromosomal material. Fertilization is the fusion of a male and a female gamete, and is part of sexual reproduction.

9. Animal species with external fertilization face significant, and sometimes formidable, hazards in reproduction, owing to the lack of protection usually afforded the gametes, zygotes, and embryos. The unconfined deposition of gametes, predation upon zygotes and embryos, and fluctuations in the physical environment all take a toll of the eggs and embryos.

### Completion Questions (Page 313)

A 1. sexual  2. sperm  3. testes  4. spermatogenesis, oogenesis   B 5. homologous  6. monoploid  7. tetrad
8. synapsis  9. crossing over  10. two   C 11. internal
12. conjugation  13. internal  D 14. morula
15. gastrula  16. yolk sac  17. amniotic   E 18. uterus

19. vas deferens, Fallopian tube  20. menstruation
21. gestation  (F)  22. testosterone  23. estrogen, pro-
gesterone  24. oviduct or Fallopian tube  25. infertility

**Multiple-Choice Questions (Page 314)**
[A] 1. (2)  2. (1)  3. (1)  4. (4)  5. (3)  [B] 6. (2)  7. (4)
8. (4)  9. (3)  10. (2)  11. (4)  12. (2)  13. (2)  14. (1)
15. (4)  16. (3)  17. (1)  18. (1)  19. (1)  20. (3)
[C] 21. (1)  22. (4)  23. (3)  24. (1)  25. (2)  26. (1)
27. (1)  28. (3)  29. (1)  (D) 30. (3)  31. (1)  32. (4)
33. (3)  34. (2)  35. (4)  36. (3)  37. (1)  38. (2)  39. (1)

40. (3)  41. (4)  42. (3)  [E] 43. (3)  44. (5)  45. (4)
46. (6)  47. (2)  48. (1)  49. (2)  (F) 50. (1)  51. (3)
52. (4)  53. (2)  54. (2)  55. (4)  56. (3)  57. (1)  58. (3)
59. (1)  60. (3)  61. (1)  62. (2)  63. (2)  64. (1)

**Chapter Test (Page 319)**
1. THE SAME  2. LESS  3. GREATER  4. LESS
5. LESS  6. (5)  7. (6)  8. (4)  9. (2)  10. (3)  11. (3)
12. (2)  13. (1)  14. (1)  15. (2)  16. (1)  17. (3)  18. (3)
19. (2)

# CHAPTER 19
# SEXUAL REPRODUCTION IN PLANTS

## Overview
The core material covers the structure and function of the flower, fertilization in plants, and the structure and function of the seed and fruit. The extended material presents alternation of generations.

## Motivation
Review with students the different methods animals utilize for sexual reproduction. Then display photographs of flowering plants and tell students that many plants also reproduce through sexual reproduction. Discuss with students their ideas on how plants accomplish fertilization despite their inability to search for a suitable mate.

## Teaching Suggestions
1. Bring to class several kinds of cut flowers. Encourage students to observe and name the different parts of the flowers, including stamens, pistils, sepals, and petals. You may wish to cut apart some of the flowers to observe the ovary and the ovule. Discuss the purpose of the different colors and scents in attracting insects to distribute pollen.

2. If possible, take students on a field trip to a nearby botanical garden or nature center to observe reproductive structures in weeds, cultivated plants, and trees. If such facilities are not available, a visit to the school grounds or a nearby vacant lot will be suitable.

3. Obtain pollen grains from a biological supply house. Demonstrate for students how to germinate the grains. Then encourage them to germinate grains on their own. Although many kinds of pollen grow in a 10% solution of sucrose in water, the optimum sugar concentration varies from 1% to 45%.

## ANSWERS TO CHAPTER 19 QUESTIONS

**Completion Questions (Page 329)**
[A] [B] [C] 1. stamen, pistil  2. stigma, style, ovary
3. anther  4. sepal, petals  5. pistillate  6. stigma
7. pollen tube  8. ovule  9. micropyle  10. ovule
11. ovary  12. hypocotyl  13. epicotyl  14. germination
15. cotyledons  (D) 16. alternation of generations
17. gametophyte  18. sporophyte  19. gametophyte
20. sporophyte

**Multiple-Choice Questions (Page 330)**
1. (4)  2. (3)  3. (2)  4. (1)  5. (3)  6. (4)  7. (2)  8. (1)
9. (3)  10. (2)  11. (2)  12. (2)  13. (4)  14. (2)  15. (1)
16. (2)  17. (1)  18. (1)  19. (4)  20. (3)  21. (3)  22. (2)
23. (2)  24. (1)  25. (2)  26. (4)  27. (2)  28. (4)  29. (3)
30. (2)  31. (1)  32. (2)

**Chapter Test (Page 332)**
1. (2)  2. (4)  3. (1)  4. (2)  5. (4)  6. (1)  7. (1)  8. (2)
9. (2)  10. (2)

## Unit 4 Portfolio Project
The following flower parts should be included in the display:
Stamens (male reproductive organs), pistils (female reproductive organs), petals, and sepals.
The following flower parts, which are involved in sexual reproduction, should be labeled:

| Structure | Function |
|---|---|
| Anther | Forms pollen grains |
| Filament | Supports the anther |
| Stigma | Deposition site of pollen grains |
| Ovary | Contains ovules, where egg nuclei form |

# UNIT FIVE
# GENETICS

Unit Five traces the beginnings of genetics and explains different genetic principles that have been developed.

The biology of DNA and Human Genetics are also explored.

# CHAPTER 20
# PATTERNS OF HEREDITY

## Overview

The core material presents Mendel's experiments and his theories on heredity, followed by the results of research on *Drosophila*. Multiple alleles and gene mutations are explained. The extended material covers probability in genetics.

## Motivation

Invite students to look at their classmates and to note varieties in hair, eye, and skin color, and in height, body shape, and facial features. Discuss with students why they think there is such a wide variety in people and what they know about how individuals inherit specific physical traits. Call on volunteers to describe how their appearance differs from, or is similar to, their brothers and sisters.

## Teaching Suggestions

**1.** To demonstrate probabilities, have each student toss a coin ten times and report the results. On the chalkboard, tabulate the number of heads and tails for each student and summarize the results of 100 trials, 200 trials, and so on. Class data of this kind usually show that as the number of trials increases, the results come closer to the theoretical percentage of 50% heads and 50% tails.

**2.** Plant pea seeds produced from hybrid parents. These seeds may be purchased from biological supply houses and some seed companies.

**3.** Fruit fly cultures may be purchased from biological supply houses. For directions on maintaining cultures and for suggestions on breeding experiments and cytological preparations, you may want to refer to the following:

- *Carolina Drosophila Manual,* by R.O. Flagg, Carolina Biological Supply Co., 1979.
- *Drosophila Guide,* by M. Demerc and B.P. Kaufmann, Carnegie Institution of Washington 1986.

**4.** As students read Chapter 20, have them complete the Critical Thinking Questions. Discuss the answers with the class.

## ANSWERS TO CHAPTER 20 QUESTIONS

### Reasoning Exercises (Page 346)

**1.** Key: T = gene for tall
t = gene for short garden peas

A. Hybrid tall × Pure tall

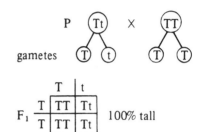

$F_1$ 100% tall

B. Hybrid tall × Short

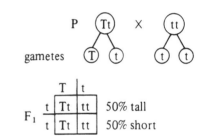

$F_1$ 50% tall
50% short

C. Hybrid tall × Hybrid tall

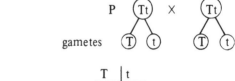

**2.** $F_1$ 75% tall
25% short

Tt × Tt → 75% tall; 25% short
Tt × TT → 100% tall
Tt × tt → 50% tall; 50% short

TT × TT → 100% tall
TT × tt → 100% tall
tt × tt → 100% short

**3.** Key: B = gene for black
b = gene for white

A. Hybrid black × White

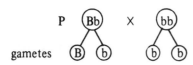

|   | B | b |
|---|---|---|
| b | Bb | bb |
| b | Bb | bb |

$F_1$  50% black  50% white

B. Pure black × Hybrid black

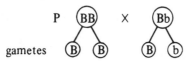

|   | B | B |
|---|---|---|
| B | BB | BB |
| b | Bb | Bb |

$F_1$  100% black

**4.** Key: W = gene for white  
w = gene for black

A. Pure white × Black

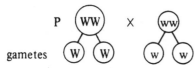

|   | W | W |
|---|---|---|
| w | Ww | Ww |
| w | Ww | Ww |

$F_1$  100% white

B. Hybrid × Hybrid

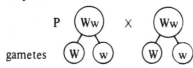

|   | W | w |
|---|---|---|
| W | WW | Ww |
| w | Ww | ww |

$F_1$  75% white  25% black

**5.** A. Hybrid black × White  
B. Hybrid black × Hybrid black  
C. Hybrid black × White  
   Hybrid black × Hybrid black  
   Hybrid black × Pure black  
D. Pure black × Pure black  
   Pure black × White  
   Hybrid black × Pure black  
E. White × White  
F. Hybrid black × White  
G. Hybrid black × Hybrid black

**6.** Mate the unknown squirrel a number of times with a pure black one.  
Key: G = gene for gray  
     g = gene for black  
Pure gray × Black

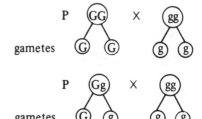

Hybrid gray × Black

|   | G | G |
|---|---|---|
| g | Gg | Gg |
| g | Gg | Gg |

$F_1$  100% gray

|   | G | g |
|---|---|---|
| g | Gg | gg |
| g | Gg | gg |

$F_1$  50% gray  50% black

If all of the offspring are gray, the unknown squirrel is pure gray; if 50% of the offspring are gray and 50% are black, the squirrel is hybrid gray. So long as only gray offspring are produced, the evidence mounts that the unknown squirrel is pure gray, but the appearance of the *first* black offspring shows it to be hybrid gray.

**7.** Key:   W = gene for white  
        B = gene for brown  
        BW = tan

A. Tan × Brown

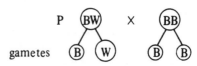

|   | B | W |
|---|---|---|
| B | BB | BW |
| B | BB | BW |

$F_1$

50% brown  
50% tan

B. Brown × White

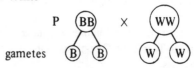

|   | B | B |
|---|---|---|
| W | BW | BW |
| W | BW | BW |

$F_1$

100% tan

**8.** Key:   R = gene for round
   L = gene for long
   LR = oval

A. Long × Round

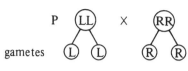

$$F_1 \quad \begin{array}{c|c|c} & L & L \\ \hline R & LR & LR \\ \hline R & LR & LR \end{array} \quad 100\% \text{ oval}$$

B. Long × Oval

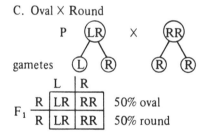

$$F_1 \quad \begin{array}{c|c|c} & L & L \\ \hline L & LL & LL \\ \hline R & LR & LR \end{array} \quad \begin{array}{l} 50\% \text{ long} \\ 50\% \text{ oval} \end{array}$$

(48 long and 52 oval is approximately a 50–50 ratio.)

C. Oval × Round

C. Oval × Round

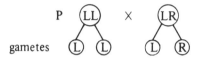

$$F_1 \quad \begin{array}{c|c|c} & L & R \\ \hline R & LR & RR \\ \hline R & LR & RR \end{array} \quad \begin{array}{l} 50\% \text{ oval} \\ 50\% \text{ round} \end{array}$$

(141 oval and 137 round is approximately a 50–50 ratio.)

**9.** Key:  B = gene for black
   b = gene for white

A. $F_1$ Hybrid black × Hybrid black

$$F_2 \quad \begin{array}{c|c|c} & B & b \\ \hline B & BB & Bb \\ \hline b & Bb & bb \end{array} \quad \begin{array}{l} 25\% \text{ pure dominant} \\ 50\% \text{ hybrid} \\ 25\% \text{ recessive} \end{array}$$

(1)  25% of 40 = 10 pure dominant *Ans.*
(2)  50% of 40 = 20 hybrid *Ans.*

B. (1) 10 white pigs would be recessive.
   (2) None would be hybrid

**10.** Key:   R = gene for red
   W = gene for white
   RW = pink

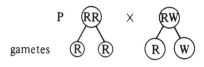

$$F_1 \quad \begin{array}{c|c|c} & R & R \\ \hline R & RR & RR \\ \hline W & RW & RW \end{array} \quad \begin{array}{l} 50\% \text{ red} \\ 50\% \text{ pink} \end{array}$$

**11.**   Key:   R = gene for red
   W = gene for white
   RW = pink

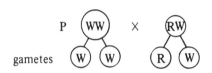

$$F_1 \quad \begin{array}{c|c|c} & W & W \\ \hline R & RW & RW \\ \hline W & WW & WW \end{array} \quad \begin{array}{l} 50\% \text{ white} \\ 50\% \text{ pink} \end{array}$$

**12.** Key:   B = gene for black
   W = gene for white
   BW = blue

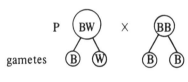

$$F_1 \quad \begin{array}{c|c|c} & B & W \\ \hline B & BB & BW \\ \hline B & BB & BW \end{array} \quad \begin{array}{l} 50\% \text{ black} \\ 50\% \text{ blue} \end{array}$$

## Reasoning Exercises (Page 358)

**1.** Key:  X = normal X chromosome
   X- = X chromosome carrying defective gene
   for hemophilia
   Y = Y chromosome

Bleeder male × Carrier female

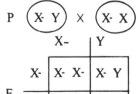

$$F_1 \quad \begin{array}{c|c|c} & X- & Y \\ \hline X- & X\text{-} X\text{-} & X\text{-} Y \\ \hline X & X\text{-} X & X Y \end{array}$$

of the males:   50% bleeders
   50% normal

of the females:   50% bleeders
   50% carriers

(Note: Since question does not specify keyed and labeled diagrams, gametes are omitted.)

**2.** Key: X = normal X chromosome
   X- = X chromosome carrying defective gene
   for color-blindness
   Y = Y chromosome

A. Normal male × Carrier female

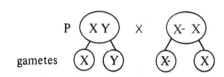

P (X Y) × (X- X)

gametes (X) (Y)   (X-) (X)

|      | X    | Y    |
|------|------|------|
| X-   | X- X | X- Y |
| X    | X X  | X Y  |

F₁

of the males:   50% normal
                50% color blind

of the females:  50% normal
                 50% carriers

B.

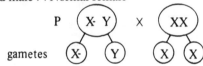

(X- Y)   (X- X-)  or  (X- X)
       (X X-)

(Answer: Father is color-blind; mother is either a carrier of color-blindness or is color-blind.)

**3.** Key: Same as problem 2.

Color-blind male × Normal female

P (X- Y) × (X X)

gametes (X-) (Y)   (X) (X)

|     | X-    | Y    |
|-----|-------|------|
| X   | X- X  | X Y  |
| X   | X- X  | X Y  |

F₁

*of the males:*   100% normal
*of the females:*  100% carriers

Normal male × Carrier female (This is one of the F₁ daughters.)

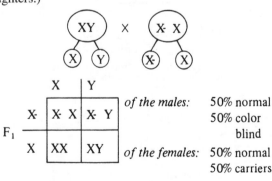

(XY) × (X- X)
(X) (Y)   (X-) (X)

|     | X     | Y    |
|-----|-------|------|
| X-  | X- X  | X- Y |
| X   | X X   | X Y  |

F₁

*of the males:*   50% normal
                  50% color blind

*of the females:*  50% normal
                   50% carriers

**4.** Key: R = gene for right-handedness
   r = gene for left-handedness

A. rr

B. RR, Rr

C. Rr × Rr ⟶ 75% right-handed,
                25% left-handed

Rr × rr ⟶ 50% right-handed,
             50% left-handed

D. Yes. Large numbers are needed to yield the expected ratios.

E. The child could be either left- or right-handed. The chances were much greater for it to have been right-handed, but large numbers are needed to yield the expected ratios. The possibility of the first child having the gene combination rr is not ruled out.

**5.** Key: H = gene for hornless
   h = gene for horned

A. Hybrid × Hybrid

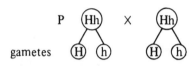

P (Hh) × (Hh)

gametes (H) (h)   (H) (h)

|     | H    | h    |
|-----|------|------|
| H   | HH   | Hh   |
| h   | Hh   | hh   |

F₁    75% hornless
      25% horned

B. Hybrid × Recessive

P (Hh) × (hh)

gametes (H) (h)   (h) (h)

|     | H    | h    |
|-----|------|------|
| h   | Hh   | hh   |
| h   | Hh   | hh   |

F₁    50% hornless
      50% horned

**Reasoning Exercises (Page 365)**

*Sample Problem* (TtYy × TtYy)

(Note: This problem is solved in text, pages 363-365, using a Punnett Square. Algebraic solution follows.)

A. Computation for the T trait

$$\frac{1}{2}T + \frac{1}{2}t$$
$$\times \frac{1}{2}T + \frac{1}{2}t$$
$$\overline{\frac{1}{4}TT + \frac{1}{4}Tt}$$
$$\frac{1}{4}Tt + \frac{1}{4}tt$$
$$\overline{\frac{1}{4}TT + \frac{1}{2}Tt + \frac{1}{4}tt}$$

B. Computation for the Y trait

$$\frac{1}{2}Y + \frac{1}{2}y$$
$$\times \frac{1}{2}Y + \frac{1}{2}y$$
$$\overline{\frac{1}{4}YY + \frac{1}{4}Yy}$$
$$\frac{1}{4}Yy + \frac{1}{4}yy$$
$$\overline{\frac{1}{4}YY + \frac{1}{2}Yy + \frac{1}{4}yy}$$

C. Multiply

$$\frac{1}{4}TT + \frac{1}{2}Tt + \frac{1}{4}tt$$
$$\times$$
$$\frac{1}{4}YY + \frac{1}{2}Yy + \frac{1}{4}yy$$

$$\frac{1}{16}TTYY + \frac{1}{8}TtYY + \frac{1}{16}ttYY + \frac{1}{8}TTYy + \frac{1}{4}TtYy + \frac{1}{8}ttYy + \frac{1}{16}TTyy + \frac{1}{8}Ttyy + \frac{1}{16}ttyy$$

1. $\frac{1}{8}TTYY + \frac{1}{8}TtYY + \frac{1}{4}TTYy + \frac{1}{4}TtYy + \frac{1}{8}TTyy + \frac{1}{8}Ttyy$
   Phenotype ratio = $\frac{3}{4}$ tall yellow : $\frac{1}{4}$ tall green

2. Symbols used for traits will vary, but phenotype ratios will not.
   AaBbGg $\times$ AaBbGg = 27/64 ABG; 9/64 Abg; 9/64 AbG; 9/64 aBG; 3/64 abG; 3/64 aBg; 3/64 Abg; 1/64 abg

## Completion Questions (Page 365)

[A] **1.** cross-pollination **2.** pure **3.** segregation **4.** 3:1
**5.** alleles **6.** pure **7.** hybrid **8.** large **9.** recessive
**10.** hybrid **11.** linked **12.** crossing-over **13.** synapsis
[B] **14.** *Drosophila melanogaster* **15.** short **16.** male
**17.** 100 [C] **18.** *0* **19.** hybrid [D] **20.** colchicine
**21.** Down's syndrome **22.** strontium-90

## Multiple-Choice Questions (Page 366)

[A] **1.** (2) **2.** (3) **3.** (1) **4.** (2) **5.** (3) **6.** (3) **7.** (3)

**8.** (1) **9.** (2) **10.** (4) **11.** (3) **12.** (2) **13.** (3) **14.** (2)
**15.** (1) **16.** (4) **17.** (3) **18.** (1) **19.** (1) **20.** (2) **21.** (3)
**22.** (1) **23.** (2) **24.** (1) **25.** (2) [B] **26.** (3) **27.** (4)
**28.** (2) **29.** (4) **30.** (1) **31.** (1) **32.** (2) **33.** (4) [C] **34.** (2)
**35.** (1) **36.** (3) **37.** (1) [D] **38.** (3) **39.** (2) **40.** (3)
**41.** (1) **42.** (4) **43.** (2) **44.** (4) **45.** (1) **46.** (4) **47.** (2)
**48.** (1)

## Chapter Test (Page 369)

**1.** (2) **2.** (2) **3.** (2) **4.** (1) **5.** (4) **6.** (3) **7.** (2) **8.** (3)
**9.** (2) **10.** (1)

# CHAPTER 21
# MOLECULAR GENETICS

## Overview

The core material explains the structure of DNA, its role in the cell, and how it was discovered. The extended material presents transcription of RNA, the genetic code, protein synthesis, gene mutations, the one gene-one polypeptide theory, and the operon theory of genetic control.

## Motivation

Review the introduction students had to DNA in Chapter 4. Point out that although the discovery of DNA's structure and function is fairly recent, people today often take this basic knowledge for granted. Ask students to think about how to take the information to build and control an entire organism, and store it in a structure as small as a cell nucleus.

## Teaching Suggestions

**1.** For an exciting account of the race to discover the structure of the DNA molecule, suggest that students read *The Double Helix,* by J.B. Watson, New York: Atheneum Publishers, 1968. This personal account of the way scientists work has aroused much controversy and could be used to stimulate a discussion on the scientific method.

**2.** Use commercial models to demonstrate the structure of the DNA molecule. Encourage students to use their ingenuity in constructing DNA models from materials such as sugar cubes, styrofoam balls, toothpicks, soda straws, and paper clips. Give students copies of Figure 21–2 from the reproducible master *DNA Structure,* on p. 66. This illustration can be used as a guide for constructing models. Have students shade each nitrogen base in a different color.

**3.** At appropriate points during their reading of Chapter 21, have students complete the Critical Thinking Questions on p. 85. Copies of Figure 21–5, *Transcription of RNA,* and Figure 21–7, *Translation: Polypeptide Synthesis,* will help students answer the questions. These illustrations are found on the reproducible masters on pp. 67 and 68.

**4.** Display the figures cited in #3 on an overhead projector and trace the steps of protein synthesis for students.

**5.** To illustrate the various ways scientists can apply their knowledge of genetics and protein synthesis, share with students the article "Mad Cows and Wild Proteins," by Mark Caldwell, *Discover,* April 1991.

## ANSWERS TO CHAPTER 21 QUESTIONS

### Reasoning Exercises (Page 382)

**1.** Each amino acid has one or more corresponding messenger RNA codons. The position of a messenger RNA codon within the messenger RNA molecule determines the placement of an amino acid in the synthesis of a polypeptide chain. No two amino acids share the same messenger RNA codons.

**2.** Answers may vary. Answers should describe the following differences: uracil vs. thymine as the complement to adenine, the single helix of RNA vs. the double helix of DNA, different enzymes involved in DNA replication vs. transcription.

**3.** Answer should include transcription of RNA, movement of RNA from the nucleus to the ribosomes in the cytoplasm, the proximity of ribosomes and messenger RNA, the role of transfer RNA, the relationship between the mRNA codons and the sequence of nitrogen bases in DNA, and the relationship between the transfer RNA anticodon and mRNA.

**4.** Long nucleotide chains with just one nitrogen base would consistently code for the same amino acid, according to the hypothesis of the genetic code. By actually showing that such a nucleotide could direct the synthesis of a polypeptide chain made up of just one amino acid, biologists began to decipher the genetic code while they demonstrated its existence.

**5.** An operon is a sequence of structural genes that act as a unit to produce a series of enzymes in a biochemical pathway.

**6.** Answers may vary. The uniform nature of the genetic code supports the idea that the biochemical mechanism of heredity is not changed by natural selection, although hereditary traits are. Accept all reasonable responses.

### Completion Questions (Page 382)

[A] **1.** function **2.** traits [B] **3.** nucleotides
**4.** replication **5.** deoxyribose [C] **6.** enzymes
**7.** polypeptide chain [D] **8.** the nucleotide sequence (or genetic code) **9.** nitrogen bases **10.** stop signals
[E] **11.** adenine **12.** ribosomal RNA **13.** enzyme
[F] **14.** DNA **15.** point **16.** nitrogen base or nucleotide; DNA [H] **17.** an operon **18.** environment

### Multiple Choice Questions (Page 383)

[A] **1.** (2) [B] **2.** (4) **3.** (3) [C] **4.** (1) **5.** (4)
[D] **6.** (1) [E] **7.** (4) **8.** (4) **9.** (3) **10.** (4) **11.** (3)
**12.** (3) **13.** (4) **14.** (2) **15.** (3) **16.** (4) **17.** (2)
[F] **18.** (4) **19.** (1) [H] **20.** (4)

### Chapter Test (Page 385)

**1.** (1) **2.** (3) **3.** (2) **4.** (4) **5.** (4) **6.** (1) **7.** (3) **8.** (1)
**9.** (1) **10.** (2) **11.** (4) **12.** (3) **13.** (2) **14.** (1)

# CHAPTER 22
# GENETICS AND PEOPLE

## Overview

The core material covers inherited traits in humans, connections between heredity and environment, genetic counseling, and the use of genetics to increase food supply. The extended material explores human genetic diseases and reports on genetic engineering.

## Motivation

Point out that recent genetic research has made it possible to alter human beings genetically. Discuss with students their ideas on this controversial research and the possible social problems and benefits that may result. You may wish to ask students a question such as, "Would you consent to having DNA that was assembled in a laboratory inserted into some of your body's cells if it meant stopping disease or giving you a better quality of life?"

## Teaching Suggestions

**1.** To expand the discussion of controversies and ethical questions arising from genetic research, you may wish to share with students the following articles:

■ "Beyond Supermouse: Changing Life's Genetic Blueprint," by Robert P. Weaver, *National Geographic,* December 1984. This article explores issues such as cloning and the use of re-combinant DNA, and also includes diagrams of DNA structure, replication, and asexual and sexual reproduction.

■ "World's Food Supply at Risk," by Robert E. Rhoades, *National Geographic,* April 1991. This article explores the weakening of food crops through genetic uniformity.

■ "A Mouse Tale," by Peter Radetsky, *Discover,* November 1991. This article reports on research of a mouse gene that repels a leukemia-causing virus.

■ "Brave New Genes," by Keith Harary, *Omni,* January 1992. This is a one-page update on the controversy surrounding artificially altered human DNA.

**2.** Distribute PTC (phenylthiocarbamide) paper to students and have them trace "tasters" and "nontasters" in the class and in their families.

**3.** You may wish to further discuss human genetic characteristics by inviting students to look at each other for the presence or absence of inheritable external characteristics, such as mid-digital hairs (hair or hairs in the middle joint of the finger), widow's peak on the scalp, attached or free earlobe, curved inward little finger, hitchhiker's thumb (thumb curves backward when extended), short big toe, and tongue rolling (the ability to roll the tongue from the sides).

**4.** Obtain karyotype photos and a human chromosome guide from a biological supply house. Have students use the guide to do a chromosomal arrangement on paper.

**5.** Invite students to bring in labels from products, such as diet sodas containing NutraSweet®, that include a warning for people who have phenylketonuria (PKU). Point out that these products contain the amino acid phenylalanine. Discuss with students what would happen if someone with PKU drank diet sodas with NutraSweet®. Refer students to Critical Thinking Questions 3–5 on p. 86 and encourage them to explain what causes PKU and the reaction affected individuals have to phenylalanine.

**6.** As students read Chapter 22, have them complete the Critical Thinking Questions at appropriate points. Discuss students' answers.

## ANSWERS TO CHAPTER 22 QUESTIONS

### Reasoning Exercises (Page 403)

**1.** Since children with PKU cannot properly metabolize phenylalanine, they are given a diet that has very little or none of this amino acid.

**2.** A defective gene fails to code for an enzyme that is needed for the production of the Hex-A enzyme.

**3.** This condition is dominant but does not develop until later in life. Some of his seemingly normal children may later develop Huntington disease, and may have already passed it on to their children, his grandchildren.

**4.** Breeding programs have developed dihybrid corn, the Beltsville turkey, and the Santa Gertrudis cattle.

**5.** Recombinant DNA technology has been used to produce human hormones, interferon, nitrogen-fixing crop plants, and bacteria that "eat" oil spills.

### Completion Questions (Page 403)

A **1.** karyotype **2.** nondisjunction B **3.** multifactorial C **4.** malaria **5.** screening **6.** nervous **7.** pure **8.** tyrosine **9.** cystic fibrosis **10.** thalassemia **11.** Huntington disease D **12.** chorionic villus sampling E **13.** four **14.** chromosomes F **15.** clone **16.** recombinant **17.** plasmid **18.** interferon **19.** legume G **20.** virus

### Multiple-Choice Questions (Page 404)

A **1.** (1) **2.** (3) B **3.** (4) C **4.** (4) **5.** (2) **6.** (4) **7.** (4) **8.** (1) D **9.** (2) **10.** (2) **11.** (3) E **12.** (3) **13.** (1) F **14.** (1) G **15.** (1)

### Chapter Test (Page 405)

**1.** (1) **2.** (3) **3.** (2) **4.** (4) **5.** (3) **6.** (2) **7.** (3) **8.** (4) **9.** (3) **10.** (4)

### Unit 5 Portfolio Projects

**1.** Student reports will vary, but should include the following information: Genetic counselors are specialized health professionals who counsel individuals and families about genetic disease and birth defects. The counselor has initial contact with families in order to obtain a family history. Genetic counselors work with patients to explain the ramifications of genetic disease. They also provide support to patients to help them cope with the emotional burdens of diagnosis of genetic disease. Genetic counselors also work with physicians and other health care professionals as part of the diagnosis and evaluation process. Additionally, genetic counselors provide education to practicing health professionals, health care students, and the public. Genetic counselors have training in biomedical science, biology, genetics, public health, and educational psychology.

**2.** Models may be based on art found on pages 75, 372, 373, and 378. Students may also do research to find illustrations of DNA and RNA on which they can base their models. Students should show that the RNA strand contains the base uracil as the complement to adenine in DNA. Labeling of the model strands should show the following complementary base pairs: Adenine with Uracil; Thymine with Adenine; Guanine with Cytosine; Cytosine with Guanine.

# UNIT SIX
# EVOLUTION

Unit Six introduces the evidences and theories of evolution and presents a detailed exploration of human evolution.

# CHAPTER 23
# EVIDENCES AND THEORIES OF EVOLUTION

## Overview

The core material presents evidences for evolution, Lamarck's theory of use and disuse, the theory of natural selection, and modern evolutionary theory. The core material also includes discussion of punctuated equilibria, evidence for evolution today, and theories on the origin of life.

## Motivation

Invite students to share observations older people have made about changes in local climate. For example, the winters used to be much colder and more snowy than they are at present. Point out that these changes are small examples of cycles and changes the earth is constantly undergoing. Then ask students how scientists know what life on the earth was like millions of years ago, before humans appeared.

## Teaching Suggestions

1. On a demonstration table, arrange specimens from the various phyla in the sequence in which their ancestral fossils appear in the geological record. Elicit the idea that this geological record represents a change from simpler to more complex forms and, in general, from marine to land forms. Correspond this demonstration with Critical Thinking Questions 2–4 on p. 87.

2. To illustrate the common ancestry of homologous structures, display actual skeletons or photographs of the skeletons of a frog, a reptile, a bird, and a human.

3. To demonstrate the differences among individuals in a species, investigate variations in beans, leaves, insect wings, heights of students, and so on. For example, measure to the nearest millimeter the length of 200 lima beans. Assort them in bottles according to length and prepare graphs to show the distribution. You might also assort scallop shells according to the number of grooves per shell. Discuss with students how a small variation that persists in a species can lead to an evolutionary change.

4. Illustrate overproduction by displaying milkweed pods, fish roe, or dandelion seed heads. Ask students to estimate how many pods, seeds, or eggs they see. Then invite students to imagine a field filled with hundreds of dandelions. Encourage students to estimate how many new dandelion plants are possible from one field.

5. Simulate Redi's experiment on spontaneous generation by substituting fruit flies and their larvae for ordinary houseflies and their maggots. Equip three jars as shown in Figure 23–13. Place the three jars inside a large sealed container into which fruit flies are released. Substitute a fruit-fly culture medium for the meat used by Redi.

## ANSWERS TO CHAPTER 23 QUESTIONS

### Reasoning Exercises (Page 422)

1. The number of fossils is limited because many organisms that died were consumed by other organisms or because they died under conditions that did not permit the preservation of their remains.

2. The heat of igneous rock would destroy fossils.

3. The relative ages of fossils may be determined by comparing the depth or age of the rocks in which they are found. Usually, the older layers of rock are at lower levels. Index organisms, which lived all over the world for brief periods of time, may be used to date the layer of rock in which they are found.

4. By determining the ratio of uranium to lead in the oldest rock, by knowing the rate at which uranium changes to lead, by assuming that this rate has remained constant, and by assuming that this rock was originally all uranium, scientists can make estimates of the length of time during which this process of change has been going on—or the age of the earth.

5. Organic evolution is the change of living things as time progresses.

6. Analogy is a similarity in function whereas homology is a similarity in evolutionary origin.

7. The similarity of bone structure in the flipper of the whale and in the foreleg of the horse indicates that they both evolved from a common ancestor. Although these appendages have different functions, they are homologous.

### Reasoning Exercises (Page 434)

1. According to the Hardy-Weinberg principle, the factors that could promote evolution are: small populations, mutations, migration, and non-random mating.

2. Darwin viewed evolution as being a slow, gradual process. According to punctuated equilibrium theory, however, evolutionary change takes place in rapid bursts, interrupted by long periods of stasis.

3. Adaptive radiation is the divergence of a population into groups having different traits.

4. Three examples that are cited for changes in gene pools today are insects resistant to DDT, bacteria resistant to

penicillin, and the melanism of the peppered moths.

**5.** According to some hypotheses, gases present in the primitive earth's atmosphere included hydrogen, water vapor, methane, and ammonia.

**6.** Photosynthesis is such a complicated biochemical process that a photosynthetic kind of organism was probably not the earliest kind of life. Moreover, photosynthesis today requires carbon dioxide, and few biologists think that this gas was present in the primitive earth's atmosphere.

## Completion Questions (Page 434)

A **1.** amber **2.** imprint **3.** tar pool **4.** igneous rock **5.** sedimentary rock **6.** uranium to lead **7.** 4.6 billion **8.** mesozoic **9.** size **10.** analogous    B-C **11.** Use and Disuse **12.** acquired characteristics **13.** Natural Selection **14.** Galapagos **15.** *On the Origin of Species*, 1859 D **16.** mutation **17.** population genetics **18.** environ-

# CHAPTER 24
# HUMAN EVOLUTION

## Overview

Chapter 24 consists of extended material that introduces anthropology, presents a phylogenetic tree of human evolution, and discusses human races.

## Motivation

Explain that evidence seems to indicate that during their short time on the earth, humans have evolved through several physical changes. Ask students to speculate what changes, if evolutionary evidence is accurate, they think humans might go through in the distant future.

## Teaching Suggestions

**1.** To help students trace the evidence of human evolution, you may wish to have them read "The Search for Our Ancestors," by Kenneth F. Weaver, and "*Homo erectus* Unearthed," by Richard Leakey and Alan Walker, *National Geographic,* November 1985. New evidence and theories regarding Neanderthals can be found in "The Deepening Conundrum of Neanderthal Man," by James Shreeve, *Smithsonian*, December 1991.

**2.** The *National Geographic* articles will also help students answer the Critical Thinking Questions on p.88. Discuss the answers with the class.

**3.** Display pictures of various kinds of primates and invite students to compare the structure of the primates' hands with that of humans. If possible, also visit a local zoo and have students observe anatomy and locomotion in apes. Review Chapter 16 during the discussion of class observations.

mental change **19.** radiation **20.** isolation **21.** opossum **22.** constancy    E **23.** few **24.** isolating    F-G **25.** melanism **26.** spontaneous generation (abiogenesis) **27.** curved **28.** biogenesis **29.** heterotrophic **30.** soup

## Multiple-Choice Questions (Page 435)

A **1.** (4) **2.** (3) **3.** (4) **4.** (1)    B-C **5.** (3) **6.** (2) **7.** (2) **8.** (2) **9.** (2) **10.** (3) **11.** (1) **12.** (2)    D **13.** (4) **14.** (1) **15.** (4) **16.** (2) **17.** (2) **18.** (1) **19.** (4) **20.** (1) **21.** (3) **22.** (4) **23.** (2)    E **24.** (4) **25.** (2)    F **26.** (4) G **27.** (2) **28.** (4) **29.** (4) **30.** (2)

## Chapter Test (Page 438)

**1.** (2) **2.** (1) **3.** (2) **4.** (2) **5.** (4) **6.** (2) **7.** (3) **8.** (3) **9.** (1) **10.** (2) **11.** (4) **12.** (2) **13.** (2) **14.** (3) **15.** (4) **16.** (2) **17.** (3) **18.** (2) **19.** (4) **20.** (1) **21.** (2) **22.** (2) **23.** (3) **24.** (2) **25.** (3)

## ANSWERS TO CHAPTER 24 QUESTIONS

### Reasoning Exercises (Page 446)

**1.** A fossil is classified as human if it seems to be bipedal—having a pelvis, for example, which indicates that it walked on two legs; its brain size is about half the size of our 1,500 cm³ capacity; and if the jaw is rounded in shape and contains small molars.

**2.** Modern humans and modern apes, such as the chimpanzee, are homologous on the molecular level because they share similar immunological reactions, arrangements of amino acids in their proteins, and sequences of nucleotides in their DNA molecules.

**3.** Johanson thinks that the *Homo* genus was a descendant of Lucy and her kin. Mary and Richard Leakey, however, think that the *Homo* lineage branched off from earlier hominids before the advent of Lucy and that these australopithecines were not our ancestors.

**4.** Anthropologists estimate social characteristics of extinct hominids by examing the bones of the animals they ate, their teeth striations, and their tools and works of art, if any, by seeing if their fossils are found in groups, and their caves had remants of fires.

### Completion Questions (Page 446)

**1.** *Australopithecus afarensis* **2.** *A. afarensis, A. africanus,* and *A. robustus* **3.** *Homo habilis* **4.** *Homo sapiens neanderthalensis, Homo sapiens sapiens* **5.** *Cro-Magnons*

### Multiple-Choice Questions (Page 446)

**1.** (2) **2.** (4) **3.** (1) **4.** (3) **5.** (3)

### Chapter Test (Page 446)

**1.** (2) **2.** (1) **3.** (3) **4.** (4) **5.** (2)

**Answers for Unit 6 Portfolio Project found on page 46.**

# UNIT SEVEN
# PLANTS AND ANIMALS IN THEIR ENVIRONMENT

Unit Seven presents and explains the biological background students need to explore and understand the interconnectedness of living things and the important environmental issues facing our world today.

# CHAPTER 25
# ECOLOGY

## Overview

The core material explains ecological organization, defines an ecosystem, and presents abiotic and biotic factors. The chapter explores energy flow and material cycles. Symbiotic relationships, succession in ecosystems, and a description of the earth's major biomes are presented as extended material.

## Motivation

Invite students to consider what they depend on for their survival. Discuss how no single organism is able to survive all by itself. It must draw air, water, and food from some other source. You may wish to point out the origins of food products that students or their families buy in the store. You might also ask students where the water they drink comes from. If students mention they do not drink much plain water, point out that the major part of all beverages is water.

## Teaching Suggestions

1. To demonstrate levels of ecological organization, take the class to the school grounds. Invite students to walk around and identify the different living populations they see, such as trees, plants and animals, insects, people, and so on. Encourage them to point out which populations seem small and which seem large.

2. If possible, arrange a field trip to a nearby natural area, such as a park, a beach, a pond, a botanical garden, a nature center, a zoo, or an aquarium. Have students observe the environment and list on paper the populations of living organisms they can identify. Then have them list the abiotic factors in the environment.

3. While on their field trip, encourage students to look for signs of ecological succession. Discuss whether the environments students observe represent climax communities. If not, ask students what kind of communities they think the environments represent.

4. Study population growth in a yeast culture as an individual laboratory exercise or as a demonstration aided by a microprojector. Use blood cell counting chambers to count yeast cells. Make serial dilutions as required.

5. When you discuss food chains and webs and pyramids of energy, distribute copies of Figures 25–7 and 25–8 from the reproducible masters on pp. 69–70. Discuss with students why the energy contained in producers on the bottom of the pyramid is so great.

Suggest that students trace with colored pencils the different relationships on the food web.

6. Ask students to turn to text pp. 460–461 and study the diagrams depicting the carbon cycle and the nitrogen cycle. Have students examine Figures 25–11 and 25–12 and identify where they as people fit into each cycle. Ask them where the carbon and nitrogen in their bodies come from, and where these elements go after leaving their bodies.

7. As a follow-up to the above activity, assign some students to research the amount of carbon and nitrogen in the adult human body. Ask them to find a percentage of each element by weight. Encourage students to compare their findings to the percentage of each element on earth. Point out the concentration of carbon and nitrogen in living organisms as compared to the relative abundance of these elements on the earth.

8. Encourage students to bring to class pictures from family vacations or pictures that relatives sent that show a biome different from the one in which they live. As an alternative, students may also bring in pictures from periodicals that show different biomes. Display the pictures and compare the biomes. Discuss the characteristics of each biome.

## ANSWERS TO CHAPTER 25 QUESTIONS

### Reasoning Exercises (Page 468)

1. Ecology is the study of the environment. This branch of science includes studying the living and non-living things in the environment and the interactions among them.

2. An ecosystem is an organized array of living organisms and non-living or physical attributes of the environment that occur in the same area or region and that interact with one another. An ecosystem contains a community of many different populations of living organisms. The interactions among the organisms and the physical aspects of the environment define the characteristics of the ecosystem.

3. A population is one part of a community. A population includes members of one species; a community contains many populations of organisms that live in the same area.

4. A community is a component of an ecosystem. A community contains many interacting populations. An ecosystem contains one or more communities of organisms.

**5.** The biosphere contains many ecosystems. An ecosystem is limited to one portion of the biosphere. All the earth's ecosystems make up the biosphere.

**6.** The biosphere is a portion of the earth. The biosphere is that portion of the earth that supports and maintains life; it is a thin zone of life on the planet and includes the atmosphere, the waters, and the land on the earth's surface.

**7.** Accept all reasonable responses that address population size and other characteristics such as density and growth.

**8.** Accept all reasonable responses that use limiting factor in its correct sense; refer to definition of limiting factor on p. 450 of textbook.

**9.** Population density is numbers per unit area. Population size is measured by numbers alone.

**10.** Producers are autotrophs; they are organisms that make their own food. Producers are at the start of most food chains and at the base of most energy pyramids. Consumers are heterotrophs that feed on other organisms.

**11.** Accept all reasonable responses that focus on abiotic factors described on pp. 453-454 of the textbook. The effects on living organisms may include effects on population characteristics, food supply, competition, symbiosis, etc.

**12.** Ectotherms depend on the environmental temperature for their body temperature. Endotherms generate heat within their bodies to maintain their body temperature.

**13.** Decomposers break down the organic matter of dead organisms and thus recycle the matter from living organisms. Decomposers make it possible for organisms in a food web to reuse matter.

**14.** Consumers do not consume all the energy contained in the producer populations, because not all of that energy is available. Of the energy they do consume, much of it is quickly burned up, not built into the bodies of the consumers. At every step in a food chain from producer to decomposer, energy is lost as heat, a by-product of the metabolism of all living organisms. For this reason, the amount of energy in a food web takes the shape of a pyramid.

**15.** "Eating high on the pyramid of energy" means consuming organisms at the end of a food chain, a few steps away from the producers in an ecosystem.

**16.** In symbiosis, at least one of the organisms benefits from the relationship, while in competition, both organisms reduce the supply of a necessary but limited resource. Competitors have a negative impact upon one another.

**17.** Accept all reasonable responses that describe mutualism, commensalism, or parasitism.

**18.** Several different responses may be acceptable. One is that the same basic material is recycled over and over again. Another is that in both cycles, the material moves from the abiotic environment to the biotic en-vironment and back again. Another is that abiotic com-partments such as the atmosphere and the soil are components of both cycles. Another is that both water and nitrogen are excreted as wastes by living organisms.

**19.** The organisms that make up a climax community have evolved to reproduce most successfully in the environment of a climax community, and outcompete other kinds of organisms that do not make up the climax community.

**20.** A climax community refers to a specific location, and includes populations of specific living organisms. A biome is an environment that covers a large geographic region and contains similar, but not necessarily identical, climax communities.

**21.** Accept all reasonable responses that refer to both biotic and abiotic components of biomes.

**22.** The neritic zone produces the most food because in this relatively shallow zone, a larger portion of the water is in the photosynthetic zone, where producers can survive.

**23.** A variety of responses are acceptable; logical and consistent statements are required. It can be argued that the food chain may contain the sequence human $\rightarrow$ mosquito $\rightarrow$ bat, as long as some of the mosquitos consumed by the bat have already fed upon the human. It can also be argued that the mosquito and the human have a symbiotic relationship, but that the bat and human are not in the same food chain because the human is not consumed.

## Completion Questions (Page 469)

[A] **1.** ecology **2.** population **3.** community **4.** size or number, density, and growth rate **5.** ecosystem **6.** biosphere **7.** limiting factor **8.** death rate and emigration **9.** birth rate and immigration **10.** numbers [B] **11.** producer **12.** herbivore or first-level consumer **13.** decomposers **14.** food web **15.** consumer **16.** possible answers include elements in the air, minerals, light, temperature, moisture, and any other components of climate and geology. **17.** saprophyte **18.** omnivores **19.** the sun **20.** consumer or omnivore **21.** more **22.** commensalism **23.** mutualism **24.** parasitism **25.** mutualism [C] **26.** the oceans **27.** the atmosphere **28.** nodules; legumes **29.** clover, soybeans, any other legume is acceptable. **30.** nitrate **31.** photosynthesis [D] **32.** succession **33.** pioneers **34.** woodland or forest [E] **35.** tropical rain forest **36.** neritic zone **37.** photosynthetic waters

## Multiple Choice Questions (Page 470)

[A] **1.** (3) **2.** (3) **3.** (1) **4.** (3) **5.** (1) **6.** (2) **7.** (2) **8.** (4) [B] **9.** (1) **10.** (3) **11.** (3) **12.** (2) **13.** (1) **14.** (1) **15.** (3) **16.** (3) **17.** (3) **18.** (1) **19.** (3) **20.** (3) **21.** (2) **22.** (4) **23.** (4) **24.** (3) **25.** (4) **26.** (1) **27.** (4) **28.** (3) [C] **29.** (1) **30.** (3) **31.** (1) **32.** (2) **33.** (2) [D] **34.** (1) **35.** (2) [E] **36.** (1) **37.** (1) **38.** (3) **39.** (5) **40.** (6) **41.** (2)

## Chapter Test (473)

**1.** (3) **2.** (4) **3.** (3) **4.** (4) **5.** (2) **6.** (4) **7.** (2) **8.** (3) **9.** (1) **10.** (4) **11.** (4) **12.** (1) **13.** (1) **14.** (4) **15.** (3)

# CHAPTER 26
# PEOPLE AND THE BIOSPHERE

## Overview

The core material covers human population growth and the corresponding increased use of energy and resources. The human impact on the biosphere and efforts to control pollution and conserve resources are also explained.

## Motivation

Invite students to look out the school window at the surrounding area. If a good view is not available, invite students to picture in their minds the neighborhood or town in which they live. Then encourage them to imagine what this area looked like before humans settled there. Discuss with students the major changes that humans have caused.

## Teaching Suggestions

1. Assign reports on topics such as the pros and cons of using insecticides and rat poison in gardens and in city areas, progress on lessening pollution in the local community, noise as a form of pollution, and the programs of various nations to control population growth.

2. Help students learn to make the presumptive test for human contamination of water through testing for *Escherichia coli*. Because standard procedures for water testing require a number of exacting controls, recommend that students contract public health authorities about any samples of drinking or bathing water that indicate pollution.

3. To help students understand that ecology is not merely a textbook topic, enlist their aid in maintaining a class bulletin board for newspaper articles about the environment. Include articles on environmental actions taken by government and citizen groups and updates on environmental issues. You may also wish to have some students collect information about local environmental issues, such as recycling programs and protests against proposed dumps or incinerators.

4. If facilities allow, direct students in constructing and maintaining their own compost heap in a corner of the school yard. Yard waste from grounds maintenance and food waste from the cafeteria might be placed in the compost heap.

5. Encourage students to bring in ingredient labels from detergent products used in their home. Examine the labels for phosphates and biodegradables. Also have students bring in labels specifying that packaging is made from recycled materials.

6. Some students may be interested in taking a poll of classmates to find out what form of energy their homes use, including natural gas, fuel oil, and electricity. Encourage students to report their findings. As an extension, ask students to present information on solar energy and wind power.

## ANSWERS TO CHAPTER 26 QUESTIONS

### Reasoning Exercises (Page 491)

1. An S-shaped growth curve represents a population that grows slowly at first and then increases rapidly before leveling off. A J-shaped growth curve represents a population that grows slowly at first and then increases rapidly without leveling off.

2. Industrialized countries can help by not taking advantage of the source of cheap wood products and beef. Answers may vary; accept all reasonable responses.

3. Slash and burn farmers clear land for planting by cutting and burning the forest trees.

4. Wetlands absorb large amounts of rain and prevent flooding, recharge and maintain the groundwater supply, serve as a purification system for runoff, and are nurseries and breeding grounds for many wildlife species.

5. Farmers can reduce erosion by practicing methods such as contour plowing and planting windbreaks and fencerows.

6. The greenhouse effect is warming of the atmosphere. Burning fossil fuels releases huge amounts of carbon dioxide into the atmosphere. This gas traps heat, like the glass on a greenhouse. Other gases contribute to this effect.

7. Bioconcentration is the process by which a substance becomes more concentrated in the bodies of organisms as it passes up the food chain from consumer to consumer.

8. Answers should include the development of pest-resistant crop strains, control of pests using predators and parasites, using small doses of pesticides to check pest populations.

### Completion Questions (Page 492)

[A] 1. immigration  2. developing  3. resources
4. ocean or marine  [B]  5. biodiversity  6. extinction
7. genes  8. taxol  9. marsh  10. summer  11. flooding
12. agriculture  13. erosion  14. fuel  [C]  15. pollutants
16. fossil  17. fossil fuels  18. energy  19. sewage
20. sanitary landfills  21. pesticide or biocide  [D]  22. extinction  23. habitat  24. Biosphere  25. endangered

### Multiple-Choice Questions (Page 493)

1. (3)  2. (1)  3. (2)  4. (1)  5. (3)  6. (2)  7. (4)  8. (3)
9. (3)  10. (2)  11. (1)  12. (3)

### Chapter Test (Page 493)

1. (1)  2. (4)  3. (4)  4. (3)  5. (1)  6. (4)  7. (1)  8. (3)
9. (1)  10. (4)

**Answers for Unit 7 Portfolio Project found on page 46.**

# APPENDIX
## ANSWERS TO LABORATORY SKILLS REVIEW QUESTIONS

**QUESTIONS (PAGES 519-525)**

**Pre-Lab Skills 1-3 (Page 519)**
1. (1) 2. (3) 3. (3) 4. (2)

**Skill 4 (Page 520)**
5. (4) 6. (1) 7. (3)

**Skill 5 (Page 520)**
8. (2) 9. (2) 10. (3) 11. (3)

**Skills 6-7 (Page 521)**
12. (3) 13. (1) 14. (4) 15. (1)

**Skill 8 (Page 521)**
16. (2) 17.(2) 18. (3) 19. (1)

**Skill 9 Page 522)**
20. (1) 21. (2) 22. (3)

**Skill 10 (Page 522)**
23. (3) 24. (3)

**Skill 11 (Page 523)**
25. (2)

**Skill 12 (Page 523)**
26. (3) 27. (2) 28. (3) 29. (1) 30. (1)

**Post-Lab Skills 13-16 (Page 523)**
31. (2)  32. (2)  33. (1)  34. (4)  35. (2)  36. (4)  37. (3)
38. (2)  39.(2)  40. (3)

# IDENTIFYING LABORATORY SKILLS AND ACTIVITIES

The objectives of the laboratory program are identified by the Regents Syllabus in Biology in the form of a list of 16 laboratory skills. This part of the Teacher's Guide suggests ways for the teacher to plan a well-rounded program of laboratory activities that will provide experiences for developing these skills.

The 16 laboratory skills are organized into pre-lab skills (1-3), laboratory activities (12), and post-lab skills (13-16).

## PRE-LAB SKILLS
Students should be able to:
- *Formulate* a question or define a problem and develop a hypothesis to be tested in an investigation.
- *Select* suitable lab materials, safety equipment, and appropriate observation methods when given a laboratory problem.
- *Distinguish* between controls and variable sin an experiment.

The pre-lab skills center on the proper design of experiments, with emphasis upon providing appropriate materials and controls. Some activities that give students experience in this aspect of inquiry are suggested below.
- *Show* how light is needed for photosynthesis.
- *Test* the action of various enzymes; for example, the effect of catalase upon hydrogen peroxide under various conditions of temperature and pH.
- *Test* the effect of adrenaline upon the heartbeat of Daphnia.
- *Compare* various juices for their content of ascorbic acid.
- *Verify* that boiling with Benedict's solution is a valid "test" for monosaccharides.

## LABORATORY ACTIVITIES
Students should be able to:
- *Identify* parts of a light microscope and their functions and focus in low and high power.
- *Determine* the size of microscopic specimens in micrometers of microns.
- *Prepare* wet mounts of plant and animal cells and apply staining techniques using iodine or methylene blue.
- *Identify* under the compound microscope such cell parts as the nucleus, cytoplasm, chloroplast, and cell wall.
- *Use* and *interpret* indicators such as pH paper, Benedict's (Fehling's) solution, iodine (Lugol's solution, and bromothymol blue.
- *Use* and *read* measurement instruments such as metric rulers, Celsius thermometers, and graduated cylinders.
- *Dissect* plant and animal specimens for the purpose of exposing major structures for suitable examination. Suggestions for specimens include seeds, flowers, earthworms, and grasshoppers.
- *Demonstrate* safety precautions involved in the heating of materials in test tubes or beakers, use of chemicals, and handling of dissection instruments.
- *Collect, organize*, and *graph* data.

## Laboratory Activities 4-7
After teaching the parts of the microscope, their functions, and precautions for use, start with live, wriggly *Tubifex* worms instead of the prosaic letter "e." (These may be purchased in local pet shops throughout most of the year.) Include a lab in which the size of the field is estimated by focusing on a plastic ruler; the millimeters are then converted to micrometers. Throughout the year, use this procedure to estimate the size of microscopic objects.

Cells the are usually studied by preparing wet mounts include cheek cells, onion skin cells, *Elodea*, and various protozoa and algae. In the unit on plant and animal physiology, study appropriate tissues such as blood and leaf epidermis. Make squash preparations of root tips.

## Laboratory Activity 8

Use pH paper in labs on urinalysis and on the effect of pH on enzyme activity. Use Benedict's and Lugol's solutions in the tests for nutrients and in the hydrolysis of starch. Use bromthymol blue to determine whether *Elodea* uses carbon dioxide when in the sunlight.

## Laboratory Activity 9

Use a metric ruler to estimate the field of a microscope and to measure the height of a spot during an experiment on thin-layer chromatography.

Use Celsius thermometers in experiments to determine the effect of temperature upon enzyme activity or on the rate of bubble formation by *Elodea* at various temperatures when in sunlight. (In this experiment, add bicarbonate of soda to the water in order to supply plenty of carbon dioxide for photosynthesis.)

Provide opportunities for students to use a graduated glass cylinder by having them prepare their own solutions, when the chemicals involved are inexpensive and safe to handle. For example, they can prepare salt solutions to study plasmolysis in *Elodea*. You may also require students to measure out specified volumes of liquids. For example, in the test for vitamin C students are asked to "Add 10 ml of indophenol to each of four test tubes."

## Laboratory Activity 10

Skill in dissection may be promoted by dissecting earthworms, grasshoppers, frogs, flowers, and fruit. Include some of your local organisms, such as seastars, fish, and unusual plants.

## Laboratory Activity 11

Among the safety precautions to emphasize are the following:

- When heating a test tube containing a liquid, point the open end away from you and anyone else.
- Wear safety goggles when heating substances or working with an open flame.
- Do not use an open flame in a room containing vapors of flammable liquids, such as alcohol and ether.
- Before touching glass tubing that has been bent or fire-polished by heat, wait a sufficient time until it has cooled. Use tongs to pick up beakers or flasks that have been heated.
- Do not attempt to insert glass tubing into rubber stoppers or to remove it, unless you have received specific instructions concerning this dangerous procedure. Report broken glassware to the teacher and receive instructions in disposing of it properly.
- Do not use any reagent or other chemical that is not clearly labeled.
- Do not taste any substances in the laboratory. (In high school laboratory instructions, students should not be required to taste anything.)
- Pour liquids slowly to avoid splashing or spilling. Do not place a wet stopper on the table top.
- Dilute acids and bases by adding the reagent slowly

to the water, not the reverse. (Adding water to concentrated sulfuric acid produces so much heat that spattering may result. In the high school biology laboratory, students should not be using concentrated acids and alkalis. However, this is a good precaution to mention if you use these in demonstrations.)

- Wash you hands at the end of each laboratory session.

Students can gain experience handling chemicals in food test experiments, in determining the effect of thyroxine upon tadpole metamorphosis, in testing for vitamin C, and in testing for blood type.

## Laboratory Activity 12

Exercises that require students to collect, organize, and/or graph data include the following:

- Prepare a very dilute starch suspension and add diastase. Test for the disappearance of starch at specified intervals. Determine the effect of temperature upon this enzymatic reaction.
- Choose one or more human genetic traits, such as PTC-taster, tongue-roller, or attached earlobe. Students can measure a sample of a given population in the school, compile data, and determine the frequency of the trait.
- Determine how long it takes the human pulse rate to return to normal after a specified period of running in place.
- A school program that permits students to go into the field provides many opportunities for collecting and graphing data. For example, how many representatives of various phyla can be found in a square meter of a vacant lot? Graph the variation of sizes, weights, and so forth, of a kind of worm, shell, insect, amphibian, seed, or fruit found in your school's locale.

## POST-LAB SKILLS

The student should be able to:

- *Make inferences* and *predictions* based upon data collected and observed.
- *Formulate* generalizations or conclusions of the investigation.
- *Assess* the limitations and assumptions of the experiment and *determine* the accuracy and readability of the experimental data and observations.
- *Determine* the accuracy and ability to reduplicate experimental data and observations.

## Laboratory Skills 13-16

These skills are concerned with formulating appropriate conclusions from an experiment. The class discussion at the end of an experiment should consider questions such as the following:

- Did the experiment have appropriate controls?
- Were sufficient trials performed to rule out the effect of chance?
- Were the conclusions more seeping than was warranted by the data?
- What assumptions are included?

# ANSWERS TO CRITICAL THINKING QUESTIONS

## ANSWERS TO CHAPTER 1

**1.** All living things carry on essential life processes, require energy, are composed of the same chemical material, and carry out basically the same chemical reactions.

**2.** transport

**3.** Nutrition. Nutrition is the overall process of obtaining and using food. Ingestion is the process by which most organisms take in food. Eating is one form of ingestion.

**4.** Sweating helps cool off the body; this keeps the internal body temperature constant.

**5.** Scientists usually test only one variable during an experiment to make sure that any observed differences between the control and the test subject are due to the variable. If two factors are variables during the same experiment, the results would probably be more difficult to understand and explain.

**6.** Accept all logical experimental protocols, which should include different amounts of water as the variable and a control plant that receives no water.

## ANSWERS TO CHAPTER 2

**1.** Taxons in common: kingdom, phylum, class, order

**2.** *Euglena* has a nucleus bound by a membrane; bacteria do not. *Euglena* lacks a cell wall, while bacteria have cell walls.

**3.** Monera; they lack a true nucleus and other membrane-bound organelles.

**4.** *Euglena* has both protozoan and algal characteristics, such as a flagellum and chloroplasts. It can make its own food like a plant cell. *Paramecium* lacks chloroplasts, and cannot make its own food.

**5.** Dicot. Dicots have flowers in groups of four or five or their multiples

**6.** Both insects and amphibians undergo a series of transformations in body form known as metamorphosis.

**7.** Fish spend their whole lives in water. Land-dwelling animals spend their whole lives on land. Amphibians have both an immature, water-dwelling stage and an adult, land-dwelling stage. The adult amphibians, like fish, lay their eggs in water. The immature amphibians, or tadpoles, use gills for respiration, not lungs.

**8.** Newly discovered organisms, both living and extinct kinds, must be described and assigned to species and other taxonomic categories. New knowledge about the biology of known organisms can alter the system of classification.

## ANSWERS TO CHAPTER 3

**1.** diaphragm

**2.** coarse-knob adjustment, fine-knob adjustment

**3.** nucleus

**4.** A selectively permeable membrane ensures that the transport of materials into and out of a cell is carefully controlled.

**5.** **a.** Cellular respiration, the energy-producing process of cells, takes place in mitochondria. Active cells require a lot of energy. **b.** The heart muscle has many mitochondria because the heart is very active. It pumps continuously.

**6.** Eukaryotes have a distinct membrane-bound nucleus; prokaryotes do not.

**7.** No, the "cells" Hooke observed were not living. Only living cells can produce new living cells.

## ANSWERS TO CHAPTER 4

**1.** **a.** four electrons **b.** one electron

**2.** two electrons

**3.** By sharing electrons the carbon atom completes its outer shell with eight electrons and each hydrogen atom completes its outer shell with two electrons.

**4.** Glycine has a hydrogen atom bonded to its R position. Alanine has a CH3 group in the R position.

**5.** Dehydration synthesis and hydrolysis are opposite reactions. In the former, water is formed as a reaction product when two molecules combine. In the latter, water reacts with a larger molecule, which splits into two smaller molecules.

**6.** Molecules can acquire enough energy to react by heating the molecules, increasing the concentrations of the reactants, or using a catalyst. In living things the catalysts are enzymes.

**7.** The shape of the active site and the chemical nature of the amino acids at the site determine which substrate molecules are welcome and which are not.

**8.** Temperature: The reaction rate increases up to 40

°C and then rapidly decreases. Concentration of enzyme and substrate: The reaction rate increases to a point and then levels off. pH: Enzymes have an optimum pH, which for many is 7.

# ANSWERS TO CHAPTER 5

**1.** White light would be produced.

**2.** Blue light has more energy because wavelength varies inversely with energy.

**3.** No, the oxygen liberated during photosynthesis comes from the water.

**4.** The illustration on the left shows a plant in which photosynthesis is taking place. The stomata are open, which means the guard cells are turgid. The guard cells become swollen when water diffuses inward due to an increased concentration of sugar. The sugar is produced by photosynthesis.

**5.** In a grasshopper, digestion is completed in the stomach and nutrients are absorbed from the stomach into the blood. In an earthworm, both digestion and absorption take place in the small intestine.

**6.** 30 molecules of carbon dioxide.

# ANSWERS TO CHAPTER 6

**1.** tail

**2.** head

**3. a.** There is a greater concentration of water molecules on side A. **b.** There is a greater concentration of glucose molecules on side B.

**4. a.** four molecules **b.** five molecules

**5.** zone of differentiation

**6.** bottom; birds are vertebrates

**7.** top; arthropods are invertebrates

**8.** bottom; humans are vertebrates

# ANSWERS TO CHAPTER 7

**1.** Plants carry out photosynthesis to produce food for energy. They obtain the energy from the food by the process of respiration.

**2.** anaerobic respiration

**3.** Fermentation is another name for anaerobic respiration.

**4. a.** 102 molecules; Every two molecules of pyruvic acid produce 34 molecules of ATP.

**5.** Three molecules. Two molecules of pyruvic acid

are produced from each glucose molecule.

**6.** The Krebs cycle produces most of the cell needs for its metabolism.

**7.** carbon dioxide, hydrogen, and ATP

**8.** no

**9.** Carbon monoxide takes the place of oxygen. Therefore, no oxygen is carried to body cells and respiration cannot take place.

**10.** Accept all logical responses, such as the transport system carries oxygen from respiratory organs to body cells and transports carbon dioxide from body cells to respiratory organs.

# ANSWERS TO CHAPTER 8

**1.** ammonia

**2.** uric acid

**3.** uric acid

**4.** ammonia

**5.** The amount of water needed to produce nitrogenous wastes varies inversely with the amount of energy.

**6.** Urea and uric acid are less toxic than ammonia. Both conserve water.

**7.** grasshopper

**8.** Because the concentration of salt is greater in the surrounding environment, water does not diffuse into the protozoa.

**9.** The lungs are the site of gas exchange between the respiratory system and the capillaries. They also excrete carbon dioxide as waste.

# ANSWERS TO CHAPTER 9

**1.** More impulses are being sent per second.

**2. a.** four impulses **b.** seven impulses

**3.** Each impulse is of the same strength and travels at the same speed in any one neuron.

**4. a.** All impulses have the same speed.

**5.** Liquid taken from the first container caused the heart in the second container to beat more slowly. A substance that dissolved in the liquid of the first container was transferred to the second container.

**6.** neurotransmitters

**7.** Auxins were prevented from passing down the stem on the unlighted side.

**8.** Agar allowed auxins to diffuse through.

**9.** Biologists think that light causes an uneven distribution of auxins. More auxins are on the unlighted side than on the lighted side. Increased growth on the unlighted side causes bending.

**10.** Insect larvae that are treated with juvenile hormone cannot mature into adults, and thus cannot reproduce. This treatment could control the population of insect pests.

# ANSWERS TO CHAPTER 10

**1.** Some scientists think that ameboid motion is caused by the sol-gel relationships. The endoplasm is in a rather fluid state called a sol. The ectoplasm is in a firmer state called a gel. At the tip of an advancing pseudopod, the sol changes to a firmer gel. At the posterior region, the gel changes to sol and is added to the flowing stream of protoplasm.

**2.** By whipping forward, a flagellum on the posterior of a protist pushes it forward.

**3.** Setae serve as anchors in the soil.

**4.** Arthropods hide to protect themselves during the vulnerable stage of molting.

**5.** The stiff skeleton of the grasshopper's legs and wings acts as levers that are pulled by the grasshopper's muscles. There is a gain in speed because the pull exerted by the grasshopper's muscles is exerted through a short distance on one end, which makes the other end move a greater distance in the same period of time.

**6.** Muscles in opposing pairs cause opposite movements. If they both contracted at the same time, neither movement would be possible.

**7.** The bones of the lower arm form a third-class lever. The elbow joint is the fulcrum, the muscles in the arm provide the effort force, and the resistant force is found below the elbow, at the lower end of the arm.

# ANSWERS TO CHAPTER 11

**1.** Answers may vary, but should include a combination of the foods listed under vitamin C totaling 100%.

**2.** Answers may vary, but should include a combination of the food listed under protein totaling 100%.

**3.** The alimentary canal is a continuous tube through which food moves. The digestive system is made up of the alimentary canal along with other digestive organs that are not found within the tube.

**4.** mouth, esophagus, stomach, small intestine, large intestine

**5.** pancreas, liver, gallbladder

**6. a.** one cell thick **b.** so that nutrients can diffuse into capillaries through the wall of a villus.

**7.** proteins

**8.** mouth

**9.** small intestine

**10.** Food sample B

**11.** vomiting

**12.** Antacids neutralize stomach acids. Bile neutralizes stomach acids in the small intestine.

**13.** mechanical digestion

**14.** Without absorption, digestion would be useless. Nutrients must be absorbed into the bloodstream so that they can be carried to body cells.

**15.** 20 Calories

# ANSWERS TO CHAPTER 12

**1.** A person with type A blood has anti-B antibodies in the plasma. The person therefore lacks anti-A antibodies and can receive type A blood. Blood type O has no antigens on its cells.

**2.** The veins would burst because they have thin walls.

**3.** Capillaries are only one cell thick. Since capillaries are the site of exchange between the blood and body cells, materials can diffuse across the capillary wall.

**4.** aorta

**5.** deoxygenated

**6.** Accept all logical responses, such as the materials car-ried by the blood change as blood circulates around the body.

**7.** There is a decreased level of oxygen.

**8.** The person might have bleeding problems due to impaired clotting.

**9.** passive immunity.

**10.** The lowered pressure causes blood to rise in the veins.

**11.** Hemoglobin is an iron-containing compound.

# ANSWERS TO CHAPTER 13

**1.** Air travels from the nose or mouth to the pharynx, to the trachea, to the bronchi, to the bronchioles, to the alveoli. Gas is exchanged with the capillaries across the alveoli.

**2.** alveoli

**3.** The nasal cavity is located between the nose and the pharynx.

**4.** esophagus, larynx

**5.** alveoli

**6.** bronchi

**7. a.** trachea and bronchi **b.** chest cavity **c.** lungs **d.** diaphragm

**8. a.** The volume in the jar decreases, increasing air pressure in the jar; therefore, air rushes out of the balloons. **b.** The volume in the jar increases, decreasing air pressure in the jar; therefore, air rushes into the balloons.

**9.** Oxygen diffuses into the capillaries from the alveoli because there is a greater concentration of oxygen molecules in the alveoli. Carbon dioxide and water diffuse into the alveoli because there is a greater concentration of these molecules in the blood. Molecules move from areas of greater concentration to areas of lesser concentration. At body cells, oxygen diffuses into the cells because there is a greater concentration of oxygen in the blood.

**10. a.** toward the right **b.** toward the left **c.** to the left

**11. a.** sneezing **b.** coughing

**12.** Gas exchange takes place in the alveoli. The function of the respiratory system is to bring oxygen to the body.

**13.** Cartilage makes up the nose, the epiglottis, the trachea, and the bronchi.

**14.** The lungs stop filling when air pressure in the chest cavity equals air pressure outside the body.

# ANSWERS TO CHAPTER 14

**1.** The urinary system is made up of the kidneys and the organs that remove urine from the body. The excretory system is made up of all the organs that remove metabolic wastes from the body, including the kidneys, skin, lungs, and liver.

**2.** Urea is a component of urine. Urine is also composed of water, uric acid, salts, some hormones, breakdown products of hemoglobin, and other organic materials.

**3.** Blood enters the kidney from the renal artery. Blood enters a nephron in the solid outer region of the kidney by a small branch of the renal artery. This branch forms a knot of capillaries called the glomerulus. Materials are filtered out of the blood in the glomerulus. The filtrate passes through a descending coiled tube, called the loop, and then through an ascending coiled loop. Blood passes through capillaries surrounding the tubes of the nephron, which eventually form the renal vein. As the filtrate passes through the nephron, reabsorption of certain materials into the blood takes place.

**4.** Blood entering a nephron contains urea. Blood leaving a nephron does not contain urea. It may also contain less water, salts, and other substances, such as drugs excreted in urine.

**5.** Proteins and blood cells are too large to pass through the filter.

**6.** The cells of the kidney tubules pass digested food molecules back into the blood by active transport.

**7.** Accept all logical responses, such as liquid intake, degree of perspiration, and intake of diuretics such as caffeine.

**8.** Most of the filtrate is reabsorbed in the nephrons.

**9.** Accept all logical reponses, which may include urinary tract infection, hormone levels, and glucose levels.

**10.** As a digestive organ, the liver produces bile which breaks down fats in the small intestine. As an excretory organ, the liver removes worn-out red blood cells and produces urea as a nitrogenous waste.

**11.** The urinary bladder stores the toxic metabolic waste urea in a place where it cannot harm cells of the body.

# ANSWERS TO CHAPTER 15

**1.** brain, spinal cord

**2.** spinal cord

**3.** cranial nerves

**4.** peripheral nerves

**5.** brain, spinal cord

**6.** Both adrenalin and glucagon raise the level of blood sugar.

**7.** Too much sugar would be taken out of the blood.

**8.** TSH, or thyroid stimulating hormone

**9.** It increases the rate of cellular metabolism.

**10.** When the level of thyroxin in the blood is high, the anterior pituitary gland is inhibited from producing TSH.

**11.** The thyroid gland decreases its production of thyroxin.

**12.** An excess of thyroxin reduces its own level.

**13.** The autonomic nervous system links the central nervous system to body systems such as the circulatory, respiratory, and digestive systems. Its nerves control the functioning of the internal organs.

**14.** Because the autonomic nervous system receives signals from the central nervous system, it does not need sensory neurons. The motor neurons in the autonomic system produce responses in internal organs.

# ANSWERS TO CHAPTER 16

**1.** While the vertebrae protect the spinal column, they must also allow the backbone some freedom of movement. With 26 vertebrae, there are a great number of joints in the backbone to permit bending and other forms of movement.

**2.** Cartilage is flexible and functions as a cushion between bones, where it reduces friction by preventing the ends of bones from rubbing against each other.

**3.** The shape of the skull does not change, so that it provides a sturdy protective case for the brain.

**4.** The radius and ulna.

**5.** The extensor or triceps muscle.

**6.** One muscle can pull a bone in one direction only. To move a bone back and forth, there must be a second muscle to pull the bone in the opposite direction.

# ANSWERS TO CHAPTER 17

**1.** Mitosis is one of the two main stages of the cell cycle. The other stage is interphase. As a result of mitosis, a parent cell produces two new daughter cells, each of which continues the cell cycle.

**2.** DNA replication is one of the events of interphase. DNA replication produces the paired chromosomes that separate during mitosis. Biologists suspect that following DNA replication, the cell must complete mitosis.

**3.** During prophase, condensation of chromatin occurs. The centrioles move to opposite ends of the cell, spindle fibers form, the nucleolus disappears, and the nuclear membrane starts to vanish rapidly.

**4.** In metaphase, fully condensed chromosomes are aligned along the cell's equator.

**5.** Anaphase is marked by the separation of the centromere and the movement of the chromatids.

**6.** The chromosomes begin to resemble the diffuse chromatin characteristic of interphase.

**7.** The spindle fibers disappear during telophase.

**8.** cytokinesis

**9.** Undifferentiated cells are more readily able to become other more specialized cells as needed.

**10.** Branches from a navel orange tree could be grafted onto normal orange trees. The grafted branches will produce seedless oranges.

# ANSWERS TO CHAPTER 18

**1.** Meiosis involves two cell divisions, which yield four cells instead of two. In meiosis, the chromosome number is reduced from diploid to monoploid.

**2. a.** four chromatids  **b.** a tetrad

**3.** The cell divides into two smaller cells.

**4.** n, or monoploid.

**5. a.** Each cell divides into two cells.  **b.** n, or monoploid.

**6.** Sperm. In spermatogenesis, the cytoplasmic divisions are equal. In oogenesis, one large cell and three smaller cells are produced after meiosis.

**7.** fertilization → cleavage → blastulation → gastrulation

**8.** testes, ovaries, oviducts, seminal vesicles, and vas deferens.

**9.** scrotum

**10.** oviduct, or Fallopian tube

**11.** uterus and vagina

**12.** seminal vesicles and prostate gland

**13.** No, because during the release of semen from the erect penis, the exit from the urinary bladder is closed.

# ANSWERS TO CHAPTER 19

**1.** Bees benefit by getting nectar. Plants benefit from pollination by bees.

**2.** Pollination is the transfer of pollen from the anther to a stigma. Fertilization is the union of egg and sperm.

**3.** Accept all reasonable responses. Answers may include: to ensure pollination of desired plants for food or decoration.

**4.** One of the sperm nuclei will fertilize the egg nucleus.

**5.** One sperm nucleus unites with one egg nucleus; a second sperm nucleus unites with the two polar bodies.

**6.** Plant seeds have no means of locomotion.

**7.** Fruit will not be eaten until the seeds are ready for dispersal.

**8.** The gametes of the gametophyte generation fuse to form a zygote. The zygote develops into the sporophyte generation.

**9.** gametophyte

**10.** sporophyte

**11.** meiosis

**12.** mitosis

**13.** The fern sporophyte is the large, conspicuous plant. The gametophyte is small. In a moss, the dominance is reversed. The gametophyte is large, and the sporophyte is small.

# ANSWERS TO CHAPTER 20

**1.** genes on a chromosome

**2. a.** dominant gene for tallness  **b.** recessive gene for tallness

3. When chromosomes separate during meiosis, their genes also separate into different gametes. Each gene of a pair separates into different gametes.

4. If the genotype were hybrid, it would possess a dominant gene and thus not show the recessive trait.

5. **a.** all 2000  **b.** 100% hybrid tall

6. **a.** 1500  **b.** 500  **c.** 25% pure tall, 50% hybrid tall, 25% pure short

7. Alleles on the same chromosome are usually not separated independently during meiosis.

8. When a pure red is crossed with a pure white, all the offspring are pink.

9. When a hybrid pink is crossed with another hybrid, the cross results in offspring with the genotype RR and WW.

10. Males carry two different sex chromosomes, the X and the Y. Depending on which of these chromosomes is carried by the sperm that fertilizes an egg (which can only carry an X), the baby will be a boy (XY) or a girl (XX).

11. Yes; 50% of the offspring could have blood type O if the type B parent has the genotype BO.

12. Independent assortment applies to genes located on different chromosomes. Linked genes cannot segregate independently during meiosis. When crossing over occurs at synapsis, genes may cross from one chromosome to another. Therefore, linked genes may become "unlinked" as a result of crossing over.

# ANSWERS TO CHAPTER 21

1. Beadle and Tatum wanted to cause gene mutations, which are produced in mold by exposure to ultraviolet light.

2. Growth occurred only in the test tube containing minimal media plus that vitamin.

3. Scientists learned that proteins often contain distinct polypeptide chains, each coded for by a different gene.

4. Scientists placed long molecules containing all adenines, or all guanines, etc., in test tubes containing all the components necessary for protein synthesis.

5. The transfer RNA anticodon is complementary to the messenger RNA codon. Therefore, the anticodon has the same sequence of three nitrogen bases as the original DNA triplet of bases that was a template for making the mRNA codon.

6. GAA, GGC.

7. The empty tRNA leaves to pick up an amino acid from the cytoplasm.

8. CAC AAC TGC GC

9. Yes, the number of nucleotides with adenine equals the number of nucleotides with thymine.

10. No, RNA contains the base uracil instead of thymine.

11. The RNA travels to the cytoplasm where it functions as messenger RNA and transfer RNA.

# ANSWERS TO CHAPTER 22

1. Cri-du-chat and Prader-Willi

2. Phenylalanine is broken down to tyrosine.

3. **a.** Phenylalanine is converted to phenylpyruvic acid.  **b.** The phenylpyruvic acid is converted to toxic derivatives that damage the nervous system. This damage leads to mental retardation.

4. **a.** What fails in a person with PKU is translation of the protein that makes up the enzyme needed to convert phenylalanine to tyrosine  **b.** People with PKU lack the gene that codes for the enzyme.

5. lightly pigmented

6. Amniotic fluid contains cells shed by the growing fetus. It also contains any secreted compounds.

7. Genetically identical disease-resistant plants can be produced.

8. Foreign DNA is inserted into the plasmid using an enzyme that makes the cut ends of DNA stick together.

9. Yes, because when the bacterium reproduces, the plasmid is duplicated. Therefore, its daughter cells receive the plasmid.

10. Answers may include interferon, human growth hormone, thymosin, somatostatin.

11. Scientists needed something to cut the DNA into small sections that could be spliced into larger strands of DNA.

12. The goal is to determine the exact nucleotide sequence of the DNA on all the human chromosomes.

# ANSWERS TO CHAPTER 23

1. The theory of floating continents showed that present day organisms that are geographically isolated were not always isolated. They became isolated as the continents drifted apart.

2. **a.** A  **b.** C

3. C

4. Any rock containing an index fossil must have formed during the time the organism lived.

5. approximately 11,460 years old.

6. Cenozoic

**7.** Ordovician

**8.** The Jurassic was marked by the dominance of dinosaurs, the appearance of birds and mammals, and the beginning of the angiosperms.

**9.** A falling leaf could become a fossil by being preserved as an imprint or mold when the leaf's form is pressed into soft sediment that later hardens.

**10.** The early embryos show that these organisms are related.

**11.** Each has a C-shape, segmentation of developing tissues, a tail, and gill slits.

**12.** pig

**13.** The bird that lays five eggs is the most successful because three offspring reproduce, which is what matters.

**14.** Darwin did not explain the basis for variation.

**15. a.** Variations, or traits, are controlled by genes. Changes in gene pools can lead to the evolution of a new species. **b.** recombination, crossing-over, mutation

**16.** water vapor, hydrogen, ammonia, methane

**17. a.** lightning **b.** rain, the ocean

**18.** amino acids

# ANSWERS TO CHAPTER 24

**1.** about 12 million years ago

**2.** about 5.5 million years ago

**3.** three species

**4.** Johanson's view

**5.** *A. robustus* was taller, had a heavier brow, and a skull crest to anchor its powerful jaw muscles. *A. africanus* was more delicate in appearance.

**6.** Accept all reasonable answers regarding a method of estimating brain capacity of the skull. One method is to fill an empty skull with sand, then pour the sand into a graduated cylinder.

**7.** Anthropologists piece together information by studying items found where extinct people lived. For example, bones tell something about diet and hunting. Charred bones show that the people used fire for cooking and possibly for keeping warm.

**8.** Anthropologists have evidence that the two groups had a common ancestor, not that one group evolved from the other.

**9.** A race consists of a regional group of individuals who have many genes in common. Nationality refers to a person's national heritage or country.

**10.** The ability to use fire enabled early humans to cook their food. Eating cooked food, which is easier to chew,

may have resulted in changes in the sizes and shapes of the teeth. The use of fire may also have given early humans a competitive advantage over other large predators in hunting large prey animals. This is because fire can be used to flush game from cover.

Answers to this question may vary greatly; accept answers that show sound reasoning.

**11.** Cro-Magnons had the same physical features as modern humans, an advanced culture, and are the most recent ancestors in fossil history.

**12.** The name means handyman; *Homo habilis* was the first hominid to make tools.

# ANSWERS TO CHAPTER 25

**1.** population

**2.** community

**3.** biosphere and ecosystem

**4.** Recent problems such as acid rain, depletion of the ozone layer, and global warming have forced ecologists to intensify study of the biosphere.

**5. a.** A **b.** A

**6.** Carrying capacity is the maximum size of a population that can be sustained in an area over a long period of time. A limiting factor is an environmental condition that limits the growth of a population. Limiting factors determine the carrying capacity.

**7.** zooplankton

**8.** algae

**9.** whales

**10.** algae

**11.** algae → zooplankton → krill → whales

**12.** snakes, weasels, owls, hawks

**13.** hawks and owls

**14.** five food chains

**15.** evaporation and transpiration

**16.** mutualistic

**17.** Lightning can convert atmospheric nitrogen into nitrates.

**18.** Plants use nitrates to build proteins

**19.** It can be changed back to free nitrogen in the atmosphere by denitrifying bacteria, or it can be converted to nitrites and nitrates by nitrifying bacteria.

**20.** They would die because they would not be able to build proteins. They are unable to use the nitrogen in the atmosphere directly.

# ANSWERS TO CHAPTER 26

1. A.D. 1650

2. about 5.2 billion

3. From 1650 to 1850, the doubling time was 200 years. From 1850 to 1930, doubling time was reduced to 80 years. From 1930 to 1970, it was reduced to 40 years. Today the doubling time is calculated to be less than 40 years. The population will have doubled before the year 2010.

4. The amount of pollution varies directly with human population density.

5. Water travels at a faster rate down a hill, which increases the amount of erosion.

6. If the polar ice caps melt, the sea level would rise. This rise in sea level would cause cities at sea level to be flooded.

7. Accept all logical responses, which may include: taking public transportation, riding a bicycle or walking, turning off unnecessary lights, and using energy efficient appliances.

8. a food chain

9. **a.** five consumers  **b.** bird

10. Birds; Bioconcentration is shown here. The small organisms took in small quantities of DDT, which did them no harm. Larger organisms ate the smaller ones, receiving many small doses of DDT and storing them in their bodies. By the time DDT reached the highest level consumers (the birds), it was sufficiently concentrated to harm them.

11. smaller fish

12. If consumers do not desire exotic wildlife, such as parrots, and wildlife products, such as ivory, then there is no demand. Without demand, it is not profitable to engage in slaughter or exploitation of wildlife.

13. Tropical rain forests are home to more than half the world's known species. These species provide people with important information and products, such as medicines. Rain forests also absorb $CO_2$, which is the cause of global warming.

14. The burning of fossil fuels releases air pollutants. By conserving energy, less fossil fuel must be burned.

15. Increase. The ozone layer protects people from the harmful ultraviolet rays of the sun.

16. These measures are meant to prevent foreign species from being introduced into another country. These foreign species may harm native species.

# Answers For Units 6 and 7 Portfolio Projects

## Unit 6 Portfolio Project
Evolution Timelines should include the following: PreCambrian, First bacteria, 3000-3500 MYA; Pre Cambria. Photosynthesis by bacteria, 2000 MYA; PreCambrian, First protists, 1000-1500 MYA; Cambrian, Animal phyla diversify in world ocena, 500-600 MYA; Ordovician, Fishes diversify, 440-500 MYA; Silurian, Plants and fungi colonize land, 400-440 MYA; Devonian, Insects and amphibians diversify, 360-400 MYA; Carboniferous, Spread of forests over land; first reptiles, 280-360 MYA; Permian, Reptiles diversify; first conifer forests, 250-280 MYA, Triassic, Earliest mammals and dinosaurs, 215-250 MYA; Jurassic, First flowering plants; dinosaurs diversify, 145-215 MYA; Cretaceous, Flowering plants and dinosaurs dominant, 65-145 MYA, Mass extinction of dinosaurs marks end of Cretaceous; Tertiary, Mammals diversify, 2-65 MYA; Quarternary, Evolution of humans

## Unit 7 Portfolio Project
Poster displays will vary. The following are examples of possible careers students might choose to research. Here is one way that students might present their findings.

| Career Name | Problem on the job | Skills/Training Requirements |
| --- | --- | --- |
| Ecologist | Measure productivity in ecosystem | Measurement; use of field equipment; Biology Training |
| Population Biologist | Project future population growth | Statistical skills Math and Biology training |
| Pollution Analyst | Test quality of water | Precision sampling and analysis Chemistry training |

# REPRODUCIBLE MASTERS:
## LIST OF ILLUSTRATIONS

| TITLE | FIGURE | PAGE |
|---|---|---|
| The Compound Microscope | Fig. 3-2 | 48 |
| An Animal Cell | Fig. 3-7 | 49 |
| A Plant Cell | Fig. 3-9 | 50 |
| The Earthworm | Figs. 5-17 and 10-8 | 51 |
| Transport Across A Cell Membrane | Fig. 6-7 | 52 |
| The Grasshopper | Fig. 9-9 | 53 |
| Paramecium | Fig. 10-4 | 54 |
| Human Heart and Circulation | Figs. 12-5 and 12-7 | 55 |
| Human Respiratory System | Fig. 13-1 | 56 |
| Human Excretory System: Kidney | Fig. 14-2 | 57 |
| Human Excretory System: Nephron | Fig. 14-3 | 58 |
| Human Skeleton | Fig. 16-2 | 59 |
| Mitosis | Figs. 17-6, 17-7, and 17-8 | 60 |
| Mitosis | Figs. 17-9, 17-10 | 61 |
| Meiosis | Fig. 18-3 | 62 |
| Human Fetus and Placenta | Fig. 18-10 | 63 |
| Human Reproductive System: Male | Fig. 18-11 | 64 |
| Human Reproductive System: Female | Fig. 18-12 | 65 |
| DNA Structure | Fig. 21-2 | 66 |
| Transcription of RNA | Fig. 21-5 | 67 |
| Translation: Polypeptide Synthesis | Fig. 21-7 | 68 |
| Pyramid of Energy | Fig. 25-7 | 69 |
| A Food Web | Fig. 25-8 | 70 |

# Figure 3–2:  The Compound Microscope

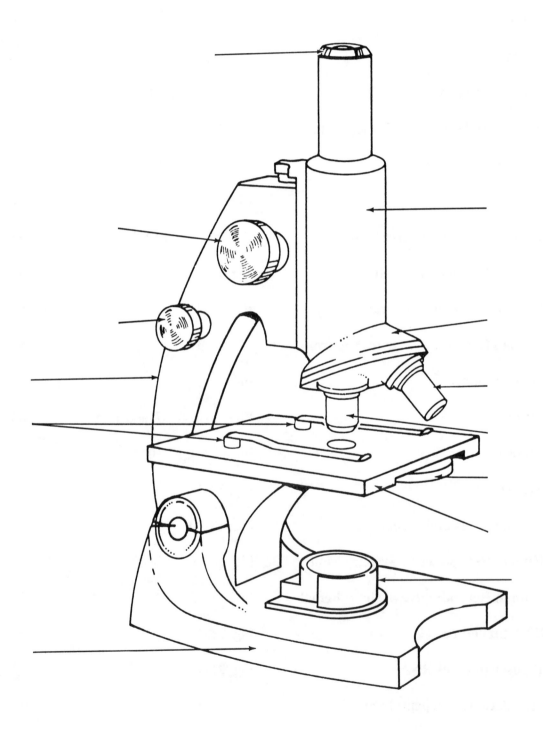

**Concepts in Modern Biology**    Copyright ©    Globe Book Company

# Figure 3–7: An Animal Cell

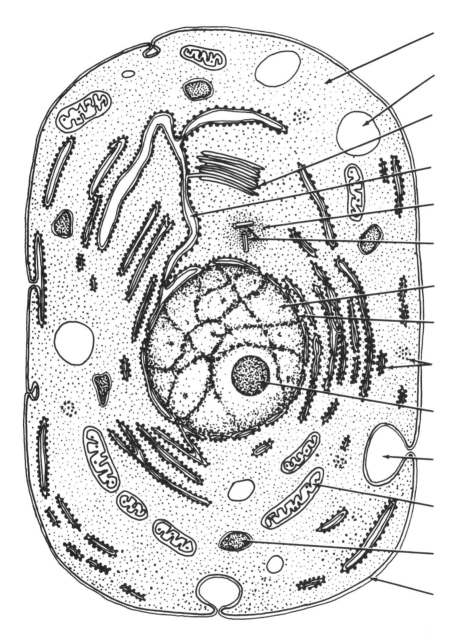

Fig. 3–7.  The fine structures of the cell

# Figure 3–9:   A Plant Cell

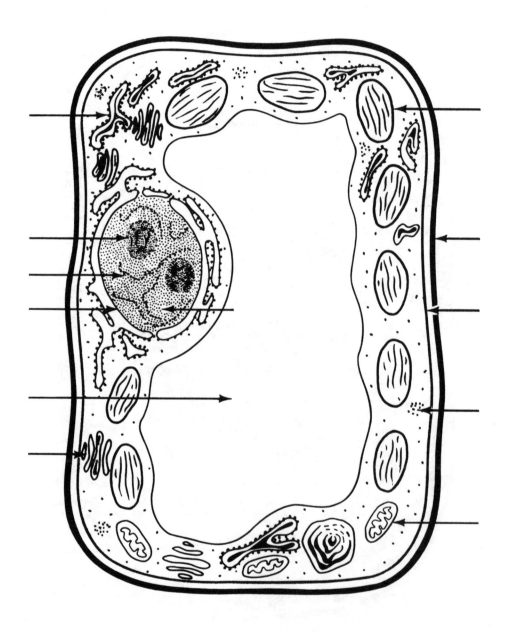

**Concepts in Modern Biology**   Copyright ©   Globe Book Company

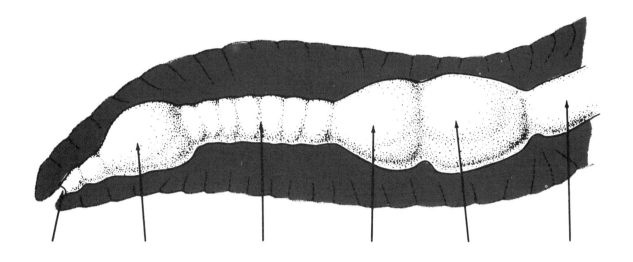

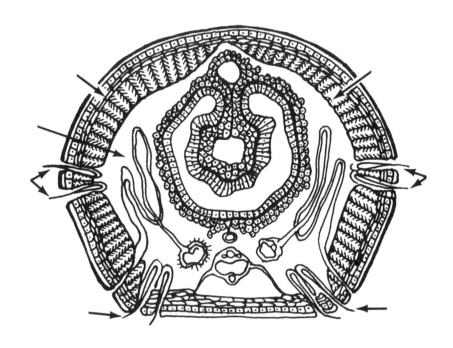

# Figure 6–7: Transport Across A Cell Membrane

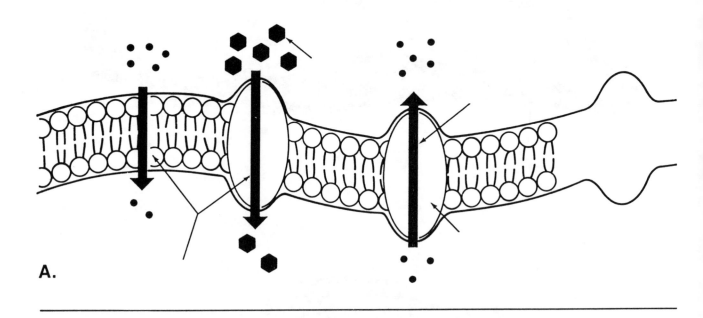

A.

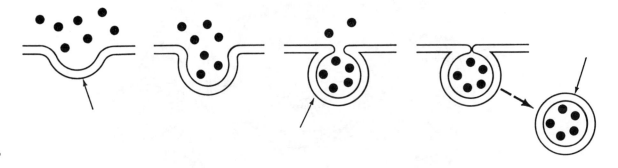

B.

**Concepts in Modern Biology**     Copyright ©     Globe Book Company

# Figure 9–9:   The Grasshopper

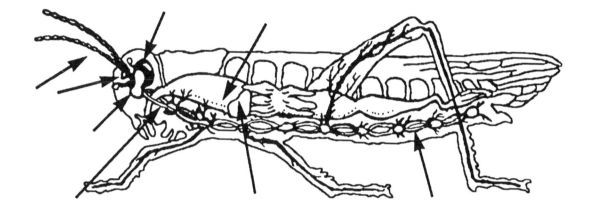

# Figure 10–4:   Paramecium

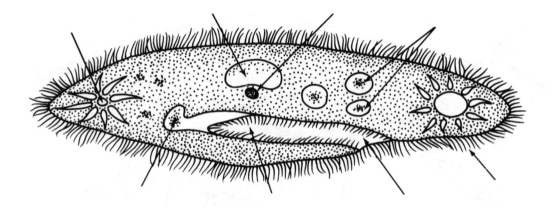

**Concepts in Modern Biology**   Copyright ©   Globe Book Company

# Figures 12–5, 12–7: Human Heart and Circulation

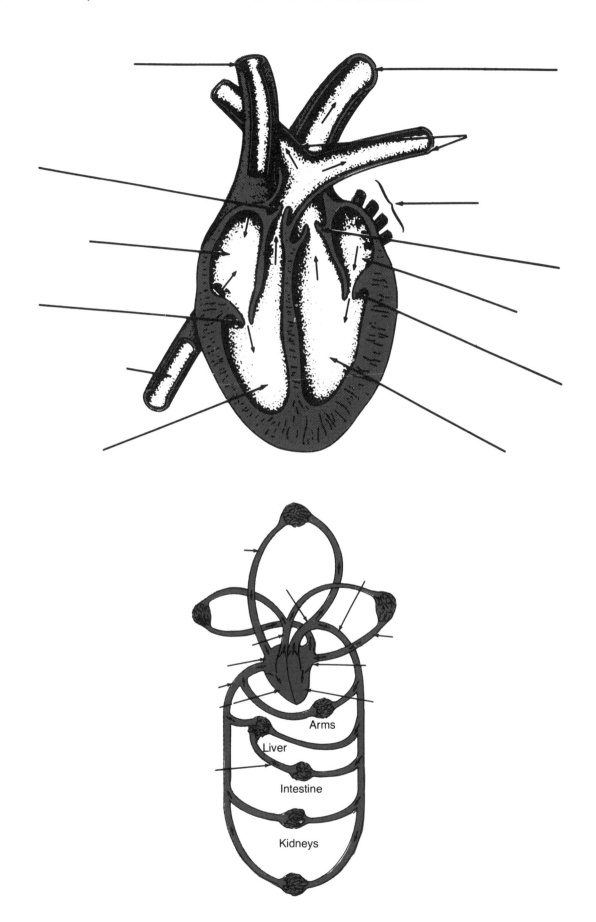

Arms

Liver

Intestine

Kidneys

# Figure 13–1: Human Respiratory System

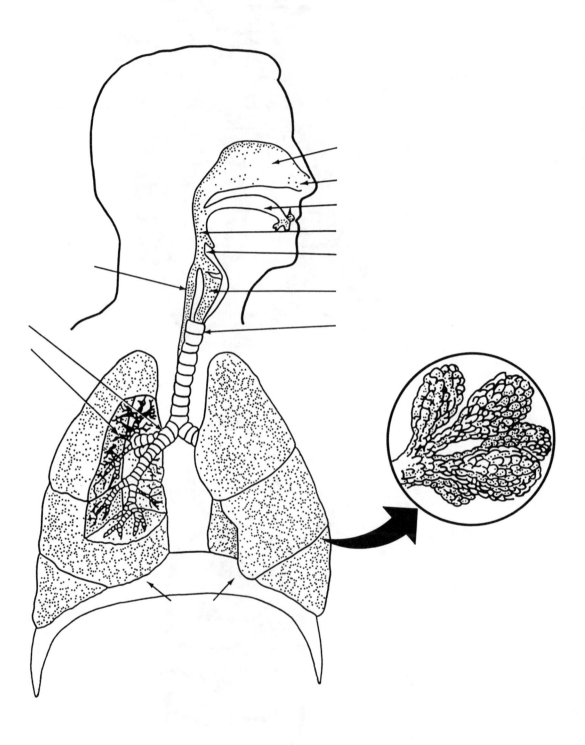

**Figure 14–2:    Human Excretory System: Kidney**

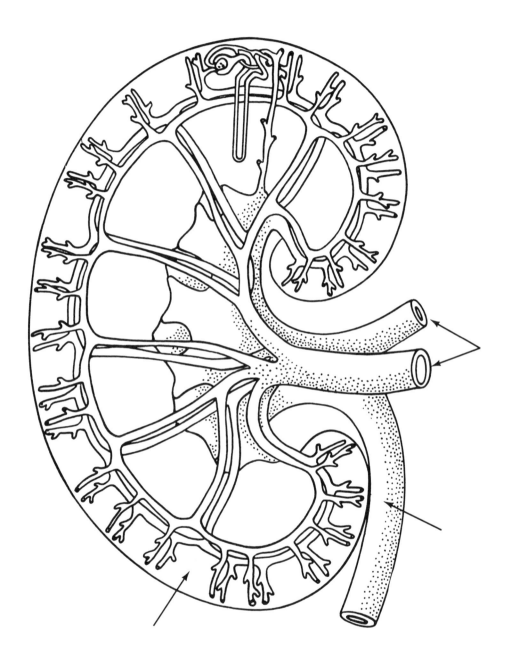

**Figure 14–3:   Human Excretory System: Nephron**

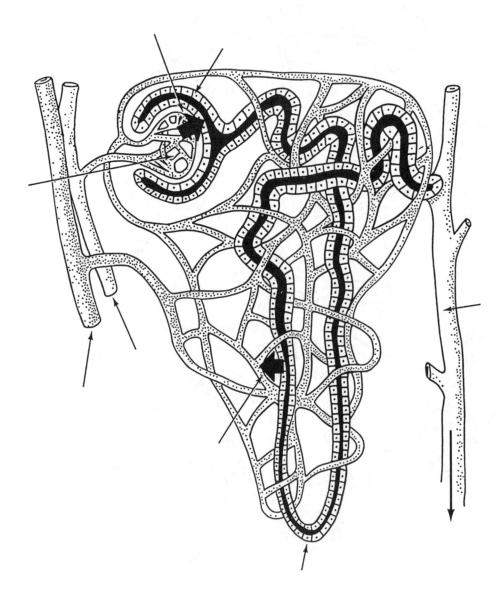

Figure 16–2:   Human Skeleton

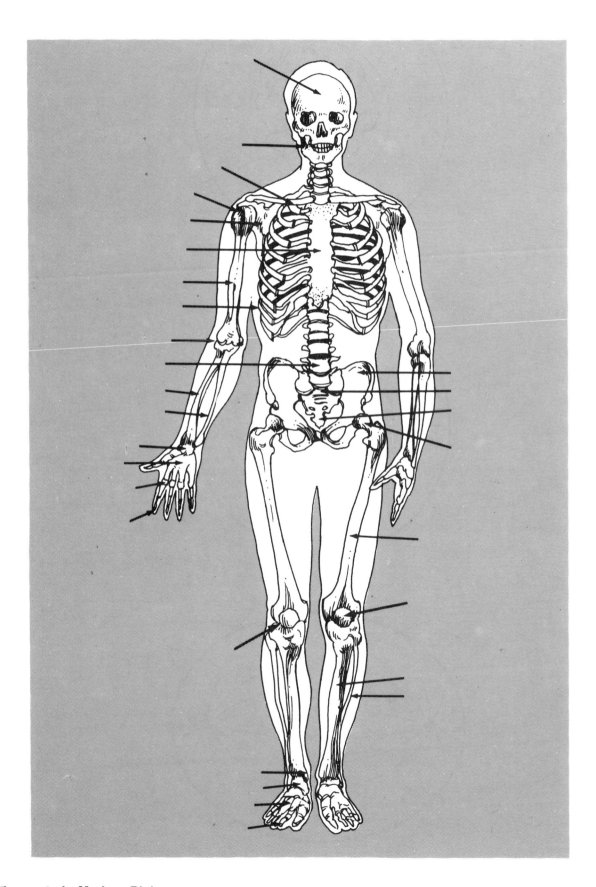

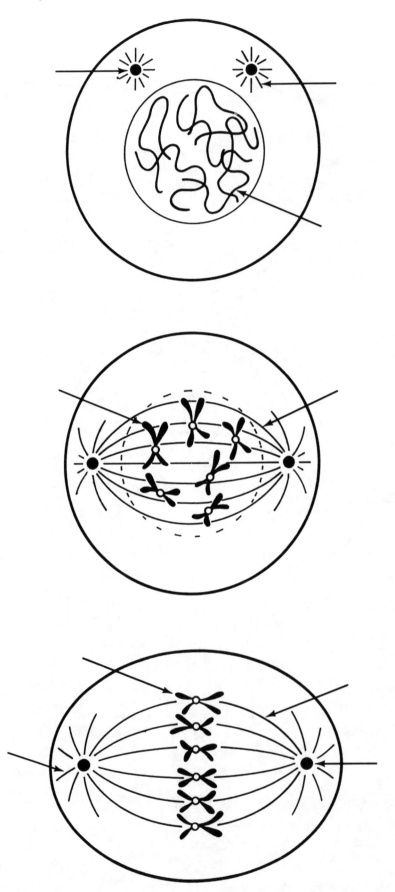

**Concepts in Modern Biology**      Copyright ©      Globe Book Company

**Figures 17-9, 17-10:    Mitosis**

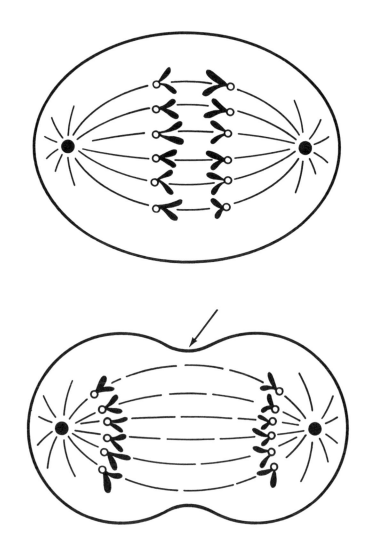

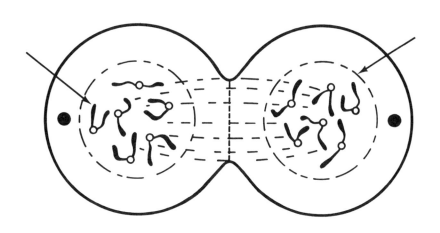

## Figure 18–3:   Meiosis

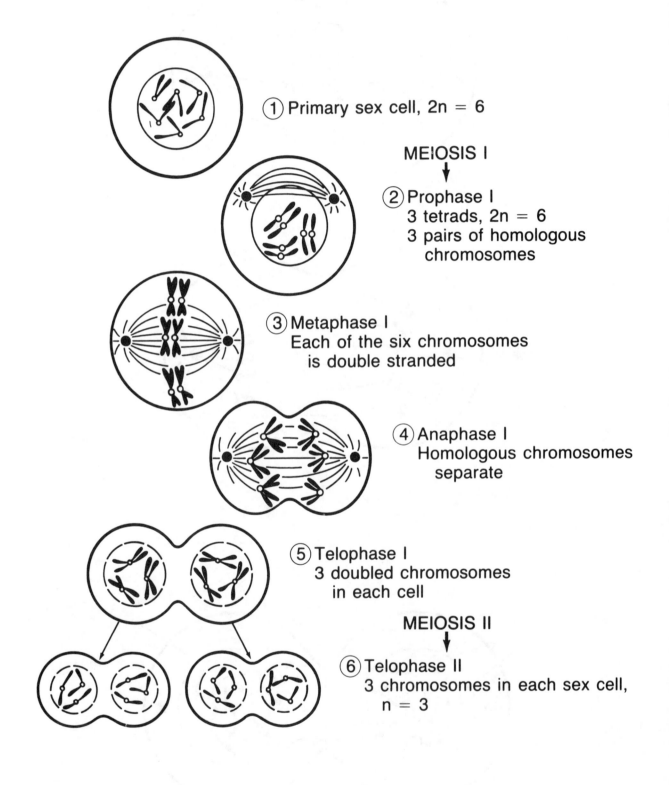

① Primary sex cell, 2n = 6

MEIOSIS I

② Prophase I
3 tetrads, 2n = 6
3 pairs of homologous
chromosomes

③ Metaphase I
Each of the six chromosomes
is double stranded

④ Anaphase I
Homologous chromosomes
separate

⑤ Telophase I
3 doubled chromosomes
in each cell

MEIOSIS II

⑥ Telophase II
3 chromosomes in each sex cell,
n = 3

**Concepts in Modern Biology**    Copyright ©    **Globe Book Company**

# Figure 18-10:  Human Fetus and Placenta

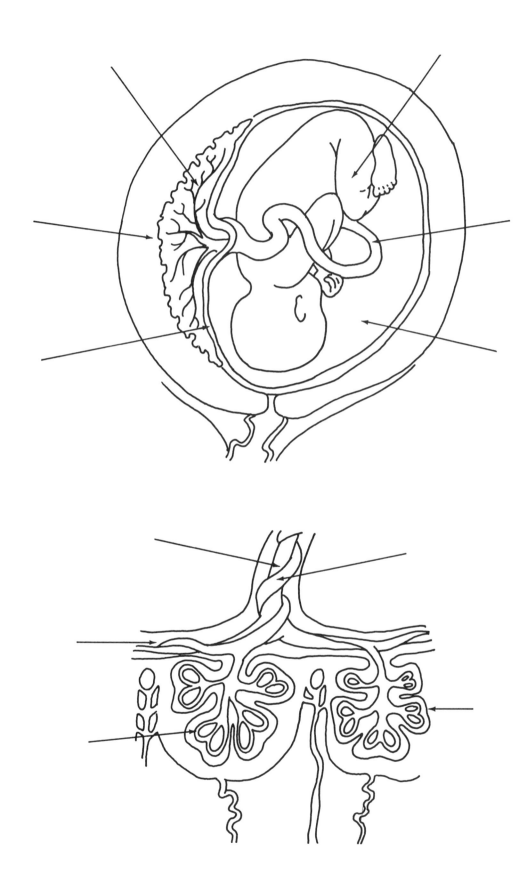

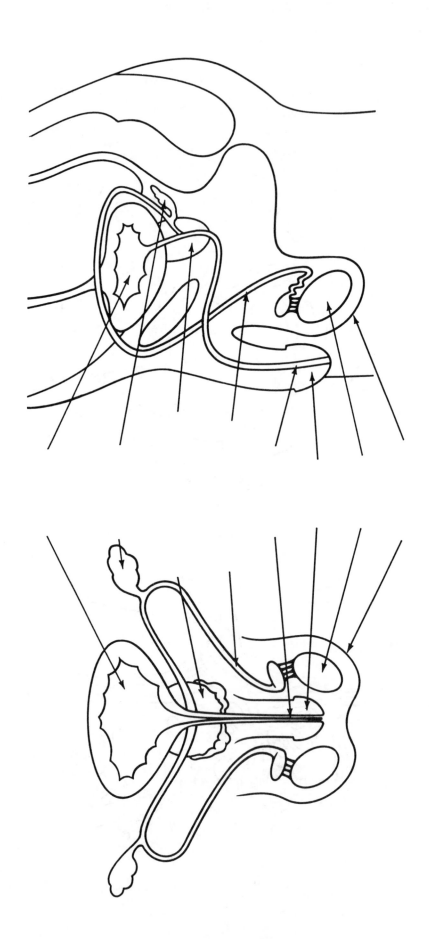

**Figure 18–11: Human Reproductive System: Male**

**Figure 18–12:   Human Reproductive System: Female**

# Figure 21-2: DNA Structure

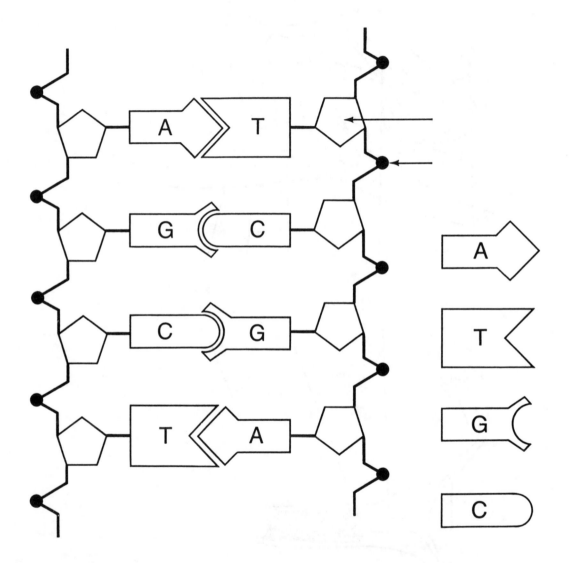

**Concepts in Modern Biology**    Copyright ©    Globe Book Company

# Figure 21–5: Transcription of RNA

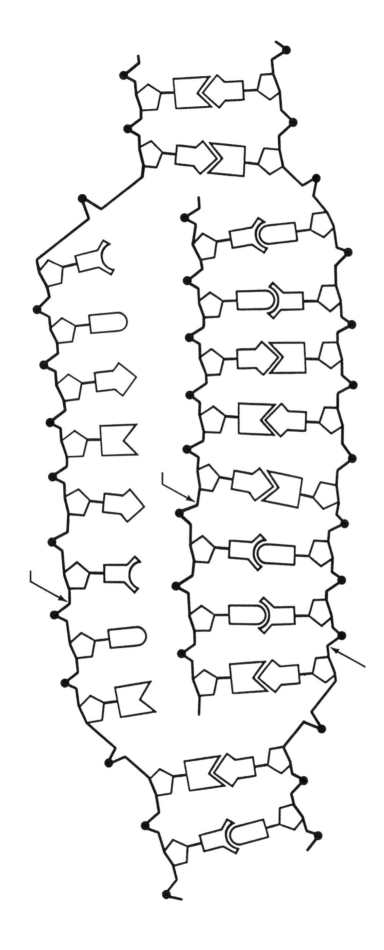

Concepts in Modern Biology

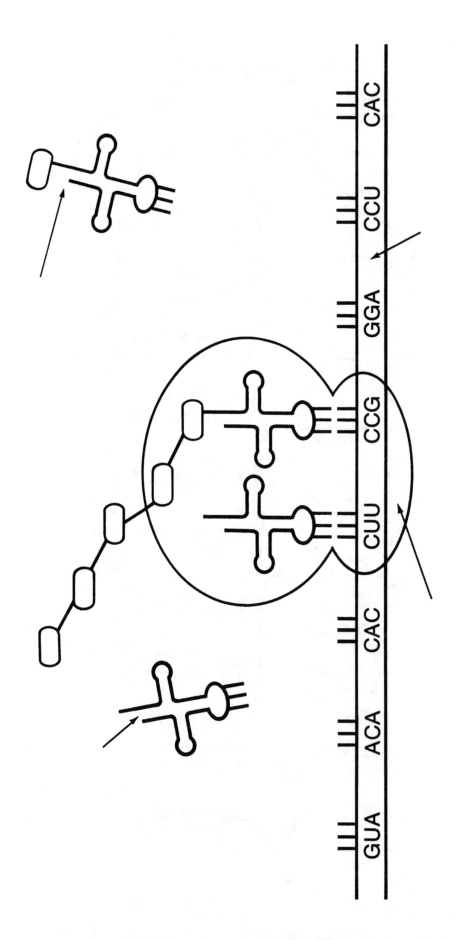

**Figure 21–7:    Translation: Polypeptide Synthesis**

# Figure 25–7: Pyramid of Energy

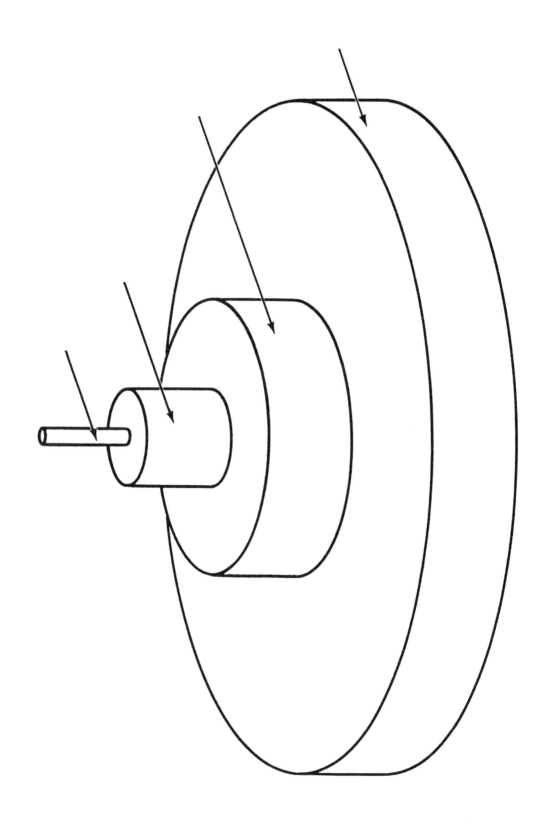

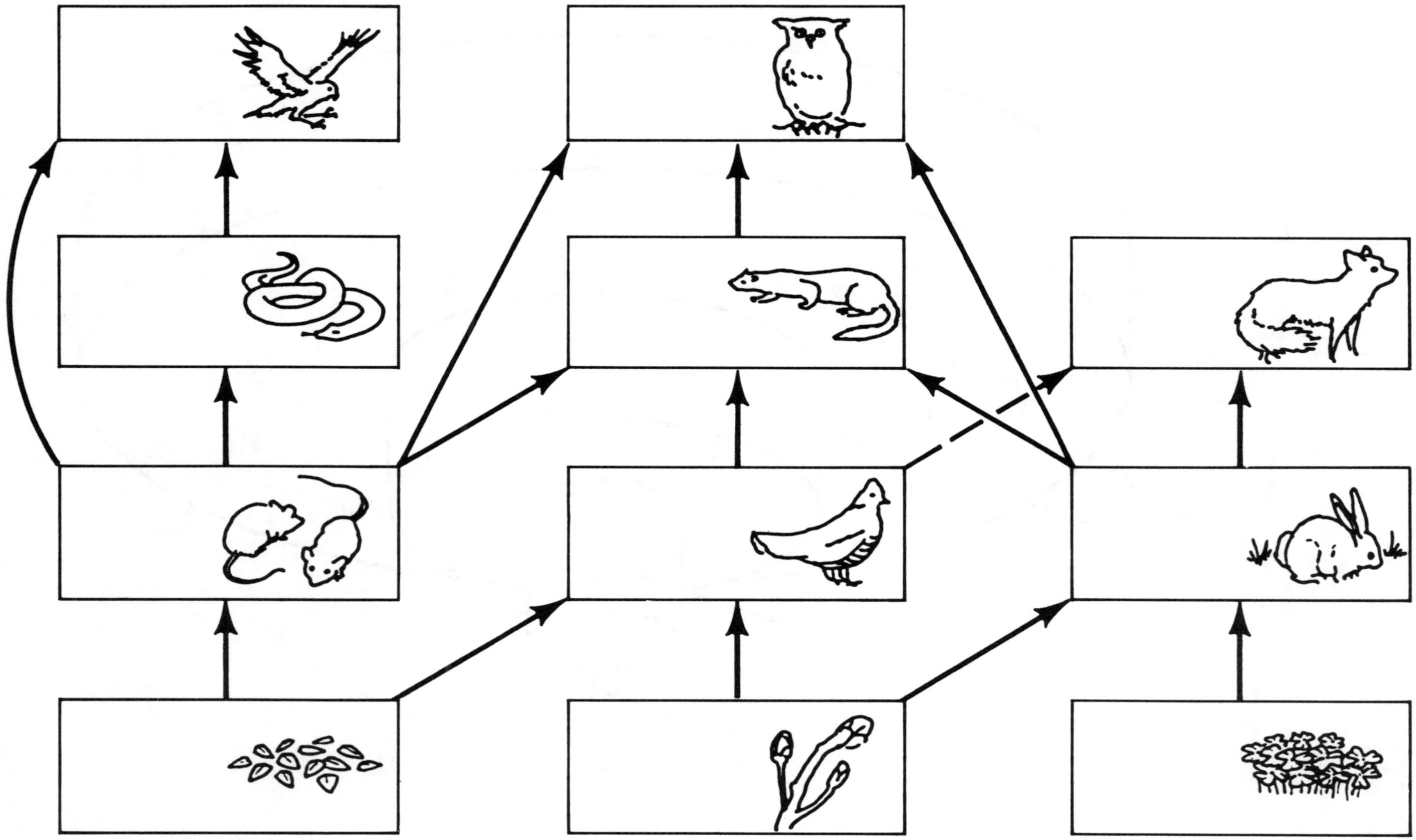

Figure 25–8:   A Food Web

# CRITICAL THINKING QUESTIONS

1. How are all living things alike?

*Base your answers to questions 2 and 3 on the chart on p. 3 of your textbook.*

2. Through which life processes could colored water move up a celery stalk?

3. Which of the following terms includes the other two: ingestion, nutrition, eating,? Explain.

4. How does sweating help maintain homeostasis?

5. Why is only one variable tested during an experiment?

6. How could you test whether plants need water? Design an experiment.

---

## Chapter 2    The Diversity of Life

1. Two organisms belong to the same family. What other taxons, or categories of classification, must they have in common?

*Study Figs. 2–2, 2–3, and 2–8, as well as the chart on p. 9 of your textbook to answer questions 2 through 4 below:*

2. Why are *Euglena* and a bacterium classified in different kingdoms?

3. To which kingdom must the organisms in Fig. 2–3 on p. 11 belong? How do you know?

4. Why can *Euglena* be classified either with the protozoa or the algae, while *Paramecium* cannot?

*Study the chart on p. 21 of your textbook to answer question 5:*

5. A plant has eight petals on each flower. Is it a monocot or a dicot? How do you know?

6. How are the life cycles of insects and amphibians similar?

7. In what ways are amphibians intermediate between fish and land-dwelling animals?

8. Why is classification of organisms an ongoing effort in biology?

# Chapter 3    Unity of Life

*Base your answers to questions 1 and 2 on the diagram of a microscope, Fig. 3–2, on p. 43 of your textbook.*

1. While viewing a specimen under high power, a student finds it necessary to have greater illumination. Which part of the microscope should the student adjust?

2. Which parts of the microscope vary the distance between the objectives and the specimen?

*Use Fig. 3–5 on p. 46 of your textbook to answer question 3.*

3. Which organelle has the greatest density?

4. Why is it important for a cell to have a selectively permeable membrane?

5. **a.** Why do active cells have many mitochondria?
   **b.** Would you expect your heart muscle to have few or many mitochondria? Explain.

6. If you were trying to discover whether an unknown organism was a prokaryote or a eukaryote, what would you look for?

7. Could the "cells" Hooke observed have produced new cells? Why or why not? Refer to Fig. 3–1 on p. 41 of your textbook.

---

# Chapter 4    The Chemistry of Living Things

*Base your answers to questions 1 through 3 on Fig. 4–9 on p. 65 of your textbook.*

1. **a.** How many electrons does carbon have in its outer shell?
   **b.** How many electrons does hydrogen have in its outer shell?

2. How many electrons does each atom of hydrogen share with the carbon atom in a molecule of methane?

3. How do the hydrogen and carbon atoms in a molecule of methane achieve complete outer shells?

4. Study Figs. 4–15 and 4–16 on p. 69 of your textbook. What is the difference between glycine and alanine?

5. Using Figs. 4–17 and 4–18 on pp. 70 and 71 of your textbook as guides, explain the relationship between dehydration synthesis and hydrolysis.

6. What are three ways molecules can acquire enough energy to react?

7. What is meant by enzyme specificity?

8. Using Figs. 4–30, 4–31, 4–32, and 4–33 on pp. 80, 81, and 82 of your textbook, explain the effect of temperature, concentration of enzymes and substrates, and pH on the rate of enzyme action.

# Chapter 5    Nutrition

1. Study Fig. 5–2 on p. 91 of your textbook. What would you expect to happen if the colors of the visible spectrum were passed through a glass prism?

2. Yellow light has a longer wavelength than blue light. Which has more energy?

3. While studying photosynthesis, a scientist used $H_2O$ and $CO_2$; the $CO_2$ contained the oxygen isotope O-18 as a tracer. Will the liberated oxygen have the tracer? Explain.

4. Study Fig. 5–12 on p. 102 of your textbook. Which diagram represents a plant in which photosynthesis is taking place, the one on the left or the one on the right? How do you know?

5. How is the stomach of a grasshopper like the small intestine of an earthworm?

6. Look at the equation for photosynthesis near the bottom of p. 94 of your textbook. How many molecules of carbon dioxide would be needed to produce 5 molecules of glucose?

# Chapter 6    Transport

*Study Fig. 6–1 on p. 119 of your textbook to answer questions 1 and 2.*

1. Which part of the phospholipid molecules making up the cell membrane is not able to mix with or take up water, the tail or the head?

2. Which part of the phospholipid molecules is able to mix with or take up water, the tail or the head?

*Base your answers to questions 3 and 4 on Fig. 6–4 on p. 121 of your textbook and on your knowledge of biology.*

3. **a.** Why will molecules of water diffuse across to side B?
   **b.** Why will molecules of glucose diffuse across to side A?

4. **a.** How many molecules of glucose will diffuse to side A to reach dynamic equilibrium?
   **b.** How many molecules of water will diffuse to side B to reach dynamic equilibrium?

5. Study Fig. 6–13B on p. 129 of your textbook. In which region of a root tip would the oldest cells be found?

*Study Fig. 6–20 on p. 136 of your textbook to answer questions 6 through 8.*

6. Which diagram shows the plan of circulation in a bird, the top one or the bottom one?

7. Which diagram shows the plan of circulation in an arthropod?

8. Which diagram shows your plan of circulation?

# Chapter 7    Respiration

1. Why do plants need to carry out both photosynthesis and respiration?

2. The bacteria that cause botulism can live in airtight canned foods. What kind of respiration do these bacteria carry out?

*Study Fig. 7–3 on p. 146 of your textbook to answer questions 3 through 5.*

3. What is the relationship between anaerobic respiration and fermentation?

4. How many molecules of ATP would be produced during aerobic respiration from six molecules of pyruvic acid?

5. How many glucose molecules are needed to form six molecules of pyruvic acid during anaerobic respiration?

*Use Fig. 7–7 on p. 150 of your textbook to answer questions 6 through 8.*

6. What is the importance of the cycle shown in the diagram?

7. What are the products of this cycle?

8. Does oxygen participate in this cycle?

9. Carbon monoxide is a gas that binds to hemoglobin more readily than oxygen. Why is this gas deadly?

10. How do your respiratory and transport systems work together?

---

# Chapter 8    Excretion

*Base your answers to questions 1 through 5 on the diagram below.*

AMMONIA        UREA        URIC ACID

more energy needed to produce $\longrightarrow$

$\longleftarrow$ more water needed to produce

1. Which nitrogenous waste requires the most water to produce?

2. Which nitrogenous waste requires the least water to produce?

3. Which nitrogenous waste requires the most energy to produce?

4. Which nitrogenous waste requires the least energy to produce?

5. What is the relationship between the amount of water and the amount of energy needed to produce nitrogenous wastes?

6. Why is it necessary for some animals to produce urea and uric acid for excretion even though this requires more energy than producing ammonia?

7. Study the chart on p. 163 of your textbook. Which organism listed in the chart conserves water the most, in comparison to its body size, to produce its nitrogenous waste?

8. Why do saltwater protozoa not absorb much water, and thus not need contractile vacuoles?

9. Why are your lungs both respiratory and excretory organs?

# Chapter 9     Regulation

*Base your answers to questions 1 through 4 on Fig. 9–4 on p. 171 of your textbook.*

1. How could you tell that the bottom diagram shows the stronger stimulus even if it was not labeled?

2. **a.** How many impulses are represented in the top diagram?
   **b.** How many impulses are represented in the bottom diagram?

3. How does the strength of each impulse in the top diagram compare to the strength of each impulse in the bottom diagram?

4. How does the speed of each impulse in the top diagram compare to the speed of each impulse in the bottom diagram?

5. Study Fig. 9–5 on p. 172 of your textbook. How did the experiment shown in the illustration provide evidence that a chemical intermediary must be involved in the pathway from nerve to muscle?

6. Some narcotics, such as codeine and morphine, act as painkillers by binding to the receptor molecules on dendrites and preventing the transfer of pain impulses. What substances do these narcotics prevent from binding to the dendrites?

*Base your answers to questions 7 through 9 on Fig. 9–10 on p. 177 of your textbook.*

7. Why did bending not occur in C when mica was inserted in the side opposite the light?

8. Why did bending occur in D when a strip of agar was used instead of mica?

9. What role do biologists think light plays in the results shown here?

10. How might agricultural scientists use insect juvenile hormone to control insects that damage crops?

---

# Chapter 10    Locomotion

1. Study Fig. 10–3 on p. 189 of your textbook. Some scientists think that the sol-gel relationships explain the ameboid movement shown in the illustration. Give their explanation.

2. Study Fig. 10–6 on p. 191 of your textbook. Describe how a flagellum could pull a protist forward.

3. What important role do setae play in an earthworm's movement?

4. Why do you think many arthropods hide in secluded areas during molting?

5. How do the appendages of the grasshopper act as levers?

6. Why would movement be impossible if muscles in opposing pairs contracted at the same time?

7. Study Fig. 10–10 on p. 193 of your textbook. How do the bones and muscles in your arm act like the lever shown in part A of the illustration?

# Chapter 11    Nutrition in Humans

*Base your answers to questions 1 and 2 on the chart on p. 204 of your textbook.*

1. What amounts of which foods could you eat every day to ensure you meet your daily requirement for vitamin C?

2. What amounts of which foods could you eat every day to ensure you meet your daily requirement for protein?

*Study Fig. 11–1 on p. 205 of your textbook to answer questions 3 through 5.*

3. What is the difference between the alimentary canal and the digestive system?

4. Which organs or glands in the illustration are part of the alimentary canal?

5. Which digestive organs are not part of the alimentary canal?

*Base your answer to question 6 on Fig. 11–2 on p. 208 of your textbook.*

6. **a.** How many cells thick is the layer of epithelial cells of an intestinal villus?
   **b.** Why is this important?

*Base your answers to questions 7 through 9 on the chart below.*

| Nutrient | Site Where Digestions Begins | Digestion Completed |
|---|---|---|
| Carbohydrates | B | small intestine |
| A | stomach | small intestine |
| Fats | small intestine | C |

7. Which nutrients are represented by letter A?

8. Which digestive organ is represented by letter B?

9. Which digestive organ is represented by letter C?

10. Ten drops of food sample A are needed to turn indophenol colorless. Six drops of food sample B turn indophenol colorless. Which food sample has the greater concentration of ascorbic acid?

11. What do you think results from reverse peristalsis in the alimentary canal?

12. How are antacids similar to bile with respect to one of bile's functions?

13. Is the action of bile mechanical or chemical digestion?

14. Why is absorption so important to the process of digestion?

15. How many Calories are needed to raise the temperature of two kilograms of water from 25°C to 35°C?

# Chapter 12   Transport in Humans

1. Examine the chart on p. 224 in your textbook. Why can a person with Type A blood receive both A and O blood?

*Study the chart on p. 226 of your textbook to answer questions 2 and 3.*

2. What would happen if blood pressure in the veins were the same as in the arteries?

3. How is the structure of capillaries adapted for their function?

*Base your answers to questions 4 through 6 on the diagram of the human circulatory system on p. 229 of your textbook.*

4. Which artery carries oxygenated blood from the heart to the rest of the body?

5. What kind of blood, oxygenated or deoxygenated, enters the right ventricle?

6. How does blood change as it circulates around the body?

7. People who live at high altitudes have an increased production of red blood cells. Why?

8. Examine Fig. 12–2 on p. 218 of your textbook. Suppose a person lacked the ability to make thromboplastin. What might happen if the person had damage to blood vessels?

9. A developing baby acquires immunity to certain diseases when it receives antibodies from its mother. Is this active or passive immunity?

10. Why does lowered air pressure in the chest cavity help venous blood flow toward the heart?

11. In cases of anemia caused by a reduced amount of hemoglobin, it is recommended that patients eat food with a lot of iron. What is the relationship between hemoglobin and iron.

# Chapter 13    Respiration in Humans

*Base your answers to questions 1 through 6 on Fig. 13–1 on p. 238 of your textbook.*

1. What path does air take from the outside of the body to the blood?

2. What is another name for air sacs?

3. Where is the nasal cavity located?

4. Which structure(s) does (do) not play a role in respiration?

5. Which structure(s) does (do) emphysema cause to degenerate?

6. Which structures are involved in an asthmatic attack?

*Base your answers to questions 7 and 8 on Fig. 13–3 on p. 240 of your textbook.*

7. **a.** What respiratory structure does the glass tubing represent?
   **b.** What structure does the jar represent?
   **c.** What structures do the balloons represent?
   **d.** What structure does the rubber sheet represent?

8. **a.** Why do the balloons deflate in diagram A?
   **b.** Why do the balloons inflate in diagram B?

9. Study Fig. 13–4 on p. 241 of your textbook. Explain the role of diffusion in the movement of the gases shown in the illustration.

*Study the equations below to answer question 10.*

A. $Hb + O_2 \longleftrightarrow HbO_2$

B. $CO_2 + H_2O \longleftrightarrow H_2CO_3$

C. $H_2CO_3 \longleftrightarrow H^+ + HCO_3^-$

10. **a.** As blood passes through the capillaries around the alveoli, in which direction would you expect reaction A above to go, toward the left, or toward the right?
    **b.** In which direction would you expect reaction B to go?
    **c.** In which direction would you expect reaction C to go?

11. **a.** What response do you think results from irritation of the nose by mucus?
    **b.** What response do you think results from irritation of the throat by mucus?

12. Why are the alveoli called the functional units of the lungs?

13. What important role does cartilage play in the respiratory system?

14. When do the lungs stop filling with air during inhalation?

# Chapter 14    Excretion in Humans

**1.** What is the difference between the urinary system and the excretory system?

**2.** What is the relationship between urea and urine?

**3.** Using Figs. 14–2 and 14–3 on p. 246 of your textbook as guides, trace the path of blood and filtrate through the kidney.

*Base your answer to questions 4 and 5 on Fig. 14–4 on p. 247 of your textbook.*

**4.** In what ways is blood entering a nephron different in composition from blood leaving a nephron?

**5.** Why do proteins and blood cells remain in the blood as it passes through Bowman's capsule?

**6.** How is active transport important in the functioning of a nephron?

**7.** About 1.4 liters of urine pass from the body per day. This amount can vary depending on certain factors. What are two of these factors?

**8.** About 180 liters of filtrate pass through the nephrons per day, at the rate of 125 ml/min. Why are only about 1.4 liters of urine produced per day?

**9.** Physicians often do a urinalysis (examination of the urine) to find out important facts about a person's general health. What are some of the things a urinalysis might reveal?

**10.** Why is the liver both a digestive organ and an excretory organ?

**11.** Urinary bladders are found in many of the vertebrate animals. What is an advantage of having a urinary bladder?

# Chapter 15  Regulation in Humans

*Base your answers to questions 1 through 5 on Fig. 15–1 on p. 254 of your textbook.*

1. Which labeled part(s) make(s) up the central nervous system?

2. Which part(s) serve(s) as the center for many reflexes?

3. Which part(s) include(s) the auditory nerves and the olfactory nerves?

4. In which part(s) might a reflex arc begin?

5. Which part(s) is (are) surrounded by meninges?

*Base your answers to questions 6 through 7 on Fig. 15–6 on p. 265 of your textbook.*

6. How do adrenaline and glucagon work together?

7. What would happen if too much insulin was injected into the body?

*Base your answers to questions 8 through 12 on Fig. 15–7 on p. 266 of your textbook.*

8. Which hormone stimulates the production of thyroxin?

9. What does thyroxin do?

10. When is the anterior pituitary gland inhibited from producing TSH?

11. What happens when less TSH is produced?

12. Why is this response an example of a negative feedback mechanism?

13. Refer to Fig. 15–4 on p. 258 of your textbook. What is the relationship of the autonomic nervous system to the central nervous system?

14. Why does the autonomic nervous system need only motor neurons?

**Concepts in Modern Biology**   Copyright ©     Globe Book Company

# Chapter 16    Locomotion in Humans

*To answer questions 1 through 3, refer to Fig. 16–3 on p. 275 of your textbook.*

1. Why do you think there are as many as 26 individual vertebrae in the backbone?

2. How does cartilage reduce the "wear and tear" on bones at joints?

3. What is the advantage of having immovable joints in the skull?

*Base your answers to questions 4 and 5 on Fig. 16–6 on p. 277 of your textbook, and Fig. 16–2, which will be provided by your teacher.*

4. Identify the arm bones that move when the flexor muscle in the upper arm contracts.

5. Which arm muscle contracts to produce the movement of reaching straight over the top of the head?

6. Why must skeletal muscles always work in pairs?

---

# Chapter 17    Asexual Reproduction

*To answer questions 1 and 2, study Fig. 17–1 on p. 282 of your textbook.*

1. What is the relationship between mitosis and the cell cycle?

2. What is the relationship between DNA replication and mitosis?

*Base your answers to questions 3 through 8 on Figs. 17–6 through 17–9. Your teacher will give you copies of these diagrams.*

3. What happens in a cell during prophase?

4. What is the major characteristic of metaphase?

5. What events occur during anaphase?

6. What happens to the chromosomes during telophase?

7. What happens to the spindle fibers during telophase?

8. What is the final step of telophase?

9. Why does having more undifferentiated cells result in a higher degree of regeneration?

10. The first navel orange tree was the result of a mutation. Describe how seedless oranges could be produced by grafting. Refer to Fig. 17–23 on p. 293 of your textbook.

# Chapter 18　Sexual Reproduction in Animals

*Base your answers to questions 1 through 6 on Fig. 18–3 on p. 300 of your textbook.*

1. How does meiosis differ from mitosis?

2. **a.** How many chromatids are there for each pair of homologous chromosomes?
   **b.** What do these chromatids make up?

3. What happens during telophase I?

4. What is the chromosome number after telophase I?

5. **a.** What happens during telophase II?
   **b.** What is the chromosome number?

6. If the four cells produced in telophase II were equal in size, would this diagram represent the production of sperm or ova? Explain.

*Refer to Fig. 18–6 on p. 303 of your textbook to answer the following question.*

7. Starting with fertilization and ending with gastrulation, write the sequence of events in the development of the embryo of an animal.

*Refer to Figs. 18–11 and 18–12 on pp. 308–309 of your textbook to answer questions 8 through 13.*

8. In humans, which reproductive structures are normally present in pairs?

9. Which structure provides the optimum temperature for sperm production?

10. In which structure does fertilization take place?

11. Through which female structures do sperm travel to reach the site of fertilization?

12. Which structure(s) in the male produce(s) fluid for sperm?

13. Can semen contain urine from the urinary bladder? Why or why not?

# Chapter 19    Sexual Reproduction in Plants

1. Refer to Fig. 19–4 on p. 323 in your textbook. A mutualistic relationship is one in which both organisms benefit. Why is the relationship between bees and certain flowering plants mutualistic?

2. What is the difference between pollination and fertilization?

3. Why might humans use artificial pollination?

4. Refer to Fig. 19–5 on p. 324 in your textbook. Which nucleus will fertilize the egg nucleus?

5. Refer to Fig. 19–6 on p. 325 in your textbook. Why is fertilization in plants called double fertilization?

6. Why are plants dependent on wind, water, and animals to disperse their seeds?

7. Usually a fruit does not ripen until its seeds are mature. Why is this important for the survival of the plant?

*Base your answers to questions 8 through 13 on Figs. 19–9 and 19–11 on pp. 327 and 329 of your textbook.*

8. What gives rise to the sporophyte generation?

9. Which generation is haploid?

10. Which generation produces asexually?

11. By what process are spores produced?

12. By what process are gametes produced?

13. How is the fern sporophyte generation different from the moss sporophyte generation?

# Chapter 20    Patterns of Heredity

*Base your answers to questions 1 through 3 on Fig. 20–1 on p. 337 of your textbook.*

1. What do the beads shown represent?

2. **a.** What does the symbol T stand for?
   **b.** What does the symbol t stand for?

3. What happens to the genes during meiosis?

4. Why is the genotype for a recessive trait always pure?

*Base your answers to questions 5 and 6 on Fig. 20–2 on p. 337 of your textbook. .*

5. **a.** If 2000 offspring were produced in the $F_1$ generation, how many would be tall?
   **b.** What would their genotype ratio be?

6. **a.** If 2000 offspring were produced in the $F_2$ generation, how many would be tall?
   **b.** How many would be short?
   **c.** What would their genotype ratio be?

7. Why does the law of independent assortment only apply if the alleles involved are on different chromosomes?

*Base your answers to questions 8 and 9 on Fig. 20–13 on p. 344 of your textbook.*

8. How does this example demonstrate incomplete dominance?

9. Why do the pure traits for flower color reappear in the $F_2$ generation?

10. Using Fig. 20–21 on p. 351 of your textbook as a guide, explain why the sex of a baby is determined by the father.

11. Using the chart on p. 356 of your textbook as a guide, determine whether type O and type B parents could have a type O offspring.

12. What is the relationship among linkage, independent assortment, and crossing over? Describe how these genetic terms compare to one another.

 **Concepts in Modern Biology**    Copyright ©    Globe Book Company

# Chapter 21  Molecular Genetics

*Base your answers to questions 1 through 3 on Fig. 21–3 on p. 374 of your textbook.*

1. Why did Beadle and Tatum expose the mold to ultraviolet radiation?

2. Why did Beadle and Tatum conclude that the mutation had destroyed the mold's ability to synthesize an enzyme needed to make thiamine?

3. Why was Beadle and Tatum's One Gene–One Enzyme theory modified to the One Gene–One Polypeptide theory?

4. How were scientists able to prove that the genetic code is a triplet code?

5. Refer to Fig. 21–6 on p. 379 of your textbook. How does the molecule shown restore the original DNA sequence?

*Base your answers to questions 6 and 7 on Fig. 21–7 on p. 380 of your textbook.*

6. What are the base sequences of the anticodons on the two tRNA molecules that are bound to the mRNA chain?

7. What happens to the empty tRNA?

8. A gene has the base sequence CAA CAA CTG CGC. Suppose the first adenine was deleted. Write the resulting triplet codons.

*Study Fig. 21–2 on p. 373 of your textbook to answer question 9.*

9. If you know the number of nucleotides with adenine, can you figure out the number of nucleotides that have another nitrogen base in the same DNA molecule?

*Study Fig. 21–5 on p. 378 of your textbook to answer questions 10 and 11.*

10. Are the nitrogen bases in the strand of RNA identical to the bases in DNA? If not, what is the difference?

11. What happens to the RNA after it is transcribed by DNA?

# Chapter 22    Genetics and People

1. Study the table on p. 389 of your textbook. Which syndrome(s) result(s) from a structural change in a chromosome?

*Base your answers to questions 2 through 4 on Fig. 22–2 on p. 391 of your textbook.*

2. What happens to phenylalanine in a normal individual?

3. **a.** What happens to phenylalanine in a person with PKU?
   **b.** Why can what happens to phenylalanine be harmful?

4. **a.** What process fails in a person with PKU?
   **b.** Why does this process fail?

5. What shade of skin would you expect a person with PKU to have?

6. Refer to Fig. 22–4 on p. 397 of your textbook. Why can amniotic fluid be used to detect certain genetic disorders such as Tay-Sachs disease?

7. How is cloning valuable to agriculture?

*Base your answers to questions 8 through 10 on Fig. 22–6 on p. 401 of your textbook.*

8. How is foreign DNA inserted into the plasmid?

9. If the foreign DNA contained the gene coding for insulin, would all bacteria descended from the parent bacterial cell produce it? Explain.

10. Name three products other than insulin that are obtained using the technology shown.

11. Why was the discovery of restriction enzymes (the enzymes that cut DNA strands) necessary before scientists could produce recombinant DNA?

12. What is the ultimate goal of the Human Genome Project?

# Chapter 23   Evolution

1. How did the plate tectonic theory help biologists explain why organisms that are geographically isolated can be related?

*Base your answers to questions 2 and 3 on Fig. 23–2 on p. 410 of your textbook.*

2. **a.** In diagram 1, which rock layer is the oldest?
   **b.** Which rock layer is the youngest?

3. In which rock layer would the fossils of more complex animals generally be found?

4. Why are index fossils useful in finding the age of a rock layer?

5. A fossil of an insect is found to have 25% of the amount of carbon 14 in a living insect. Approximately how old is the fossil?

*Base your answers to questions 6 through 8 on the Geologic Time Scale on p. 413 of your textbook.*

6. What is the present day era?

7. During what period did trilobites live?

8. What events marked the Jurassic period?

9. How could a falling leaf become a fossil?

*Base your answers to questions 10 through 12 on Fig. 23–10 on p. 420 of your textbook.*

10. What do the early embryos show about the relationships among the turtle, the chicken, the pig, and the human?

11. What features do the early embryos have in common?

12. From your observation of the later embryos, which organism shown do you think is most closely related to humans?

13. Which bird is the most successful in an evolutionary sense: the bird that lays 10 eggs, of which 7 hatch and 2 reproduce, or the bird that lays 5 eggs, of which 4 hatch and 3 reproduce?

14. What was one weakness in Darwin's original theory of evolution?

15. **a.** How has the development of modern genetics supported Darwin's theory of evolution?
    **b.** What are three things that can cause change in a gene pool?

*Base your answers to questions 16 through 18 on Fig. 23–15 on p. 433 of your textbook.*

16. According to scientists, what gases made up the primitive atmosphere?

17. **a.** What did the sparks in Miller's experiment represent?
    **b.** What did the water represent?

18. What organic compounds were produced in the flask?

# Chapter 24    Human Evolution

*Base your answers to questions 1 through 4 on Fig. 24–2 on p. 442 of your textbook.*

1. When are hominids thought to have separated from the ape lineage?

2. When did the first humanlike primates live?

3. How many species are classified in the genus *Homo* ?

4. Whose view of human lineage does this phylogenetic tree best represent, Donald Johanson's or the Leakeys'?

5. How did *A. robustus* differ in appearance from *A. africanus*?

6. How might you estimate, in cubic centimeters, the brain capacity of a human skull?

7. How do anthropologists gather evidence about the social and cultural patterns of extinct people?

8. Why is it incorrect to state that anthropologists have evidence that humans descended from monkeys, chimpanzees, or gorillas?

9. What is the difference between race and nationality?

10. How might the ability to use fire have affected the development of early humans?

11. Why do scientists consider Cro-Magnons the most immediate ancestors of modern humans?

12. Why is the name *Homo habilis* appropriate for the name of this hominid species?

*Concepts in Modern Biology*    Copyright ©    Globe Book Company

# Chapter 25    Environment

*Base your answers to questions 1 through 3 on Fig. 25–1 on p. 447 of your textbook.*

1. Which group includes all the people in your neighborhood?

2. Which group includes all the people and other organisms in your neighborhood?

3. Which level(s) of organization include(s) both living and nonliving things?

4. Why have ecologists been forced to study the biosphere more intensely in recent years?

5. **a.** Refer to Fig. 25–2 on p. 449 of your textbook. In which diagram is the density of trees greater, A or B?
   **b.** Which diagram shows the population with a greater chance of cross-pollination?

6. What is the relationship between carrying capacity and limiting factors?

*Base your answers to questions 7 through 11 on Fig. 25–7 on p. 456 of your textbook.*

7. Which level of consumers contains the largest percentage of total stored energy?

8. Which of the organisms are autotrophic?

9. Which level contains the fewest organisms?

10. Which level contains the greatest amount of energy?

11. What is a possible food chain sequence derived from this energy diagram?

*Base your answers to questions 12 through 14 on Fig. 25–8 on p. 456 of your textbook.*

12. Which organisms are consumers of mice?

13. Which organisms are likely to have the smallest populations?

14. How many different food chains include buds as producers?

15. Study Fig. 25–10 on p. 459 of your textbook. Which process(es) put(s) water back into the atmosphere?

*Base your answers to questions 16 through 20 on Fig. 25–12 on p. 461 of your textbook.*

16. What kind of relationship do nitrogen-fixing bacteria and legumes have?

17. What role does lightning play in the nitrogen cycle?

18. How do plants use nitrates?

19. What happens to the ammonia produced by bacteria of decay?

20. What would happen to plants and animals if there were no nitrogen-fixing bacteria?

# Chapter 26    People and the Biosphere

*Base your answers to questions 1 through 3 on Fig. 26–1 on p. 475 of your textbook.*

1. In what year did the human population reach one-half billion?

2. What is the present human population?

3. How has the human population doubling time changed from A.D. 1650 to the present?

4. What is the relationship between pollution and human population density?

5. Why is flat land in less danger of eroding than hilly land?

6. How might global warming affect sea level cities in the future?

7. What are three ways in which you can help conserve energy?

*Base your answers to questions 8 through 11 on Fig. 26–10 on p. 487 of your textbook.*

8. What is shown in the diagram?

9. **a.** How many consumers are shown?
   **b.** What is the highest level consumer?

10. Which organisms were most harmed by DDT? Explain.

11. Which organism has a lower concentration of DDT, the smaller fish or the larger fish?

12. How can consumer demand for certain items affect the conservation of wildlife?

13. Why are tropical rain forests vital to the biosphere?

14. How does energy conservation lessen the amount of air pollution?

15. Do you expect the incidence of skin cancer to increase or decrease if nothing is done to protect the ozone layer? Explain.

16. Many nations do not allow wild plants or animals to be taken across their borders. Why do you think these measures are necessary?